DATE DUE

DEC. 08 2003			

DEMCO 38-296

Christmas Everywhere

other books by the same author:

HEIGH-HO FOR HALLOWEEN!
ONE THOUSAND POEMS FOR CHILDREN
POEMS FOR RED LETTER DAYS
RED LETTER DAYS
THIRTEEN GHOSTLY YARNS

in collaboration with Janette Woolsey:

IT'S TIME FOR CHRISTMAS
IT'S TIME FOR EASTER
IT'S TIME FOR THANKSGIVING
IT'S TIME TO GIVE A PLAY
NEW PLAYS FOR RED LETTER DAYS

CHRISTMAS

Written and Compiled by

Elizabeth Hough Sechrist

Illustrations by Elsie Jane McCorkell

EVERYWHERE

A Book of Christmas Customs of Many Lands

New Revised and Enlarged Edition

MACRAE SMITH COMPANY: PHILADELPHIA

New Revised Edition. Third Printing.

Library of Congress Catalog Card Number 62-13303

Manufactured in the United States of America

6210

ACKNOWLEDGMENTS

The compiler wishes to express her thanks and appreciation to the following publishers for their kind permission to include their works in this volume:

Century Company for "Christmas Customs in Switzerland" by Marie Widmer from *St. Nicholas Magazine,* and "Christmas in Bethlehem" by Edwin S. Wallace from *St. Nicholas Christmas Book.* Thomas Y. Crowell Company for "Christmas at Luchitsa" from *A Boy in Serbia* by E. C. Davies. Doubleday & Company, Inc. for "Christmas on the Gaspé" by Marguerite de Angeli from *Petite Suzanne* by Marguerite de Angeli, copyright 1937 by Marguerite de Angeli; reprinted by permission of Doubleday & Company, Inc. E. P. Dutton & Co., Inc. for "A Christmas Carol" by Phillips Brooks from the book *Christmas Songs and Easter Carols* by Phillips Brooks, published by E. P. Dutton & Co., Inc.; reprinted with their permission. Little, Brown & Company for "Yuletide Joys" from *Gerda in Sweden* by Etta Blaisdell McDonald and Julia Dalrymple. Lothrop, Lee and Shepard Company for "Unique Christmas Customs in Norway" from *When I Was A Boy in Norway* by Dr. D. O. Hall; "Yuletide in Spain" from *Yuletide in Many Lands* by M. P. Pringle and Clara A. Urann; and "Christmas Cheer" from *When I Was a Boy in Rumania* by J. S. Van Teslaar. The Macmillan Company for "Christmas in Paris" from *Paris* by Margery Williams Bianco.

Dedicated to the memory of

MY MOTHER

INTRODUCTION

ONE DAY NEAR CHRISTMAS WHEN THE CHILDREN OF THE
Public Library were standing in line for the Story Hour,
two boys came to a disagreement as to whether or not there
was a Santa Claus! It started us all to thinking. There were
two sides to the argument, of course. Some of the boys and
girls were very skeptical about the matter. The rest of us
were just as firm in our belief that Santa Claus is real. With
such differences of opinion, we decided that the best way to
settle the discussion was to make a thorough investigation.
The idea occurred to us to find out what other children
believed about Santa Claus. Why not make a search into
other countries, and discover how the boys and girls of the
nations far away celebrate their Christmas?

So that is what we did. We delved here and there, search-
ing wherever we thought we might discover something new
about Christmas. We soon found that there were many
strange customs in the celebration of the Yuletide in other
lands, and most of these customs were much older than our
own. But in spite of the fact that there were such differences
in ceremonies and celebrations, and even in the languages
spoken, there was one thing that was the same everywhere—
the universal Christmas spirit! It made us feel more than
ever that the boys and girls all over the world were very
much like one big family, after all!

7

And what about Santa Claus? Oh, he was there! It was not difficult to recognize him, even though his name was not always the same. He was Santa, Pelznickel, Tomten, St. Nicholas, and lo, even the Christ-Child! We seemed to find him in every place where the children had the joy of Christmas in their hearts. And with this discovery we decided that Santa Claus was very much like the bluebird sought by Tyltyl and Mytyl. He was real to all the boys and girls who knew how and where to look for him.

To those who have been interested in the search, and to all those boys and girls for whom the Spirit of Christmas is a reality, this collection of stories is presented.

ELIZABETH HOUGH SECHRIST

CONTENTS

9

10 *Contents*

A CHRISTMAS CAROL

Christmas in lands of the fir tree and pine,
Christmas in lands of the palm tree and vine;
Christmas where snow peaks stand solemn and white,
Christmas where cornfields lie sunny and bright;
Everywhere, everywhere Christmas tonight!

Christmas where children are hopeful and gay,
Christmas where old men are patient and gray,
Christmas where peace, like a dove in its flight,
Broods o'er brave men in the thick of the fight;
Everywhere, everywhere Christmas tonight!

For the Christ Child who comes is the Master of all;
No palace too great—no cottage too small.
The angels who welcome Him sing from the height,
"In the city of David a King in His might."
Everywhere, everywhere Christmas tonight!

Then let every heart keep its Christmas within
Christ's pity for sorrow, Christ's hatred of sin,
Christ's care for the weakest, Christ's courage for right,
Christ's dread of the darkness, Christ's love of the light,
Everywhere, everywhere Christmas tonight!

So the stars of the midnight which compass us round,
Shall see a strange glory and hear a sweet sound,
And cry, "Look! the earth is aflame with delight,
O sons of the morning rejoice at the sight."
Everywhere, everywhere Christmas tonight!

PHILLIPS BROOKS

Christmas Everywhere

THE UNITED STATES

Christmas Under the Fifty Stars

CHRISTMAS UNDER THE FIFTY STARS OF THE FLAG OF THE
United States of America: what is it like?

If several children were asked to name their favorite time
of all the Christmas season, some might reply that they like
best that moment when they open their gifts. Others might
say it is Christmas dinner and still others that it is their
first glimpse of the Christmas tree that they cherish most.
But surely some would say that the days just *before* Christmas are the best time of all. This is the time of preparation
for the big day itself.

What makes it such a gay and exciting time? Well, everywhere we look we are reminded of Christmas. The streets are gay with festive decorations and lights, and thronged with people rushing here and there. In "the square" or at the most prominent intersection there is always a big community Christmas tree. Trees for the people to buy and take home are there too, wherever the vendors can find space to display them. On almost every corner there is a "Santa Claus's helper" standing beside a kettle to collect the coins that will be used for Christmas dinners for the needy. Then, as one walks along the street there are the shop windows to admire. Shopkeepers have displayed their most attractive wares in an appealing way to entice buyers into their stores. Some of the windows are like glimpses of fairyland, with lifelike characters from the stories children love; others are scenes of Santa's workshop with animated figures of Santa Claus and his elves going about their tasks. Inside, the stores are decorated in the spirit of the season. Merchandise to appeal to every taste is on display. The toy department is crowded with a pushing, jostling throng of boys and girls whose gaze is filled with wonderment. All toys imaginable—and many not ever to be imagined—are there, from walking, talking dolls to miniature space stations and jet aircraft. At one end of the room another throng is waiting in line where Santa Claus is holding interviews with the small fry as he listens to their Christmas dreams and desires.

It is safe to say that every merchant in the United States has put forth his best efforts at this season of the year and has planned for it months in advance. His sales at Christmas account for one-fourth of the entire year's trade. He must hire extra help to take care of the Christmas buyers and this gives employment to many full- or part-time workers. All the manufacturers of Christmas merchandise start early in the year to produce the immense flood of goods that will be needed by the retail stores at this time.

When an American family sets up the Christmas tree in a corner of the living room, the role it plays in industry is seldom considered. This particular tree is only one of many millions grown in controlled forests to supply the demand during the short Christmas season. The trees chosen for the market are usually young ones that have been cut from the thicker portions of the wide area in which they are grown. Their removal helps the growth of the other trees by giving them more space and light in which to develop. The most popular Christmas trees are white and yellow pine, spruce and balsam. Most of them are grown in the northern areas of the United States, but some come from Canadian forests. In addition to the many millions of trees, greens for decorating are sold in great quantities. Laurel, mistletoe, eucalyptus and pine cones are sold by the Christmas tree merchants.

Our national custom of exchanging greeting-cards at Christmas has also developed into a large business. Each year many thousands of people are employed in the designing and manufacture of the cards. Thousands more are put to work in the United States Post Office to handle and deliver the huge stacks of mail.

Shopping for gifts, selecting the Christmas tree and

greens, sending Yuletide greeting cards—these are only a few of the pre-Christmas activities that take place in preparing for the big day. There is the decorating to be done, not only of the homes but also of the schools, churches and other public places, for scarcely a spot is neglected. Most communities offer prizes for the best decorations on porches and lawns. Streets in residential sections are so transformed that people like to drive about just to see the Christmas lights and representations. Bright lights glow from houses and lawns and shrubbery. Santa and his reindeer are seen riding on the rooftops, while porches show life-size figures of Santa Claus filling stockings at a huge fireplace. Probably the most popular Christmas scenes to have appeared in recent years are those of the Nativity and the three Wise Men. These are truly the most representative of all at this season that celebrates Christ's birthday.

A miniature Bethlehem, or crêche, is also displayed in many homes across America. The boys and girls in a family will often make this a project of their own when it comes time to decorate for Christmas. The background is made of pine boughs or simulated moss, rocks and artificial snow. Then the manger and all the tiny figures that have been kept from year to year are given their proper places. There are the figures of Mary and Joseph beside the infant Jesus lying in a manger, the shepherds who came to worship, and the Three Wise Men: Melchior, ruler of Nubia and Arabia; Caspar, king of Tarsus; Balthasar, the dark-skinned king of Ethiopia. Others are present too, including the lowly sheep and oxen of the manger scene, and camels and goats and little barnyard animals.

The figurines used in the Nativity scene are sometimes made of carved wood and these are treasured by the families who own them. But most of the modern ones are made of painted clay or plaster of Paris and are quite inexpensive. Some people are fortunate in owning hand-painted ones. In the town of Bryn Athyn, Pennsylvania, the women of the Swedenborgian Church annually paint hundreds of colorful little figures with great attention to detail. Long before Christmas they are sent to the missions of the church in lands across the sea.

Preparing the food for the feast of Christmas is another pre-Christmas activity. During the week the markets are flooded with good things to eat. Drawn turkeys ready to be stuffed and popped into the roasting pan, chickens, ham, pork roasts; salad greens and celery; oranges and other fruits, and pumpkins; mincemeat, pickles, raisins, fat figs, stuffed dates and chopped fruit for cakes; candies, nuts and cookies! They are all there for the buying.

Cookies are a very important goodie in the Christmas fare of our country as they are in many other nations of the world. Every family has its own special favorites. Moravian families in Pennsylvania have old German recipes for all sorts of delicious cookies. These have such enchanting names as *Leckerli* (meaning "delicious morsel"), *Lebkuchen, Pfeffernuss* (spice nuts), *Springerle* made in molds, and *Belsnickelkuche.* This last is a cake that in olden days was offered to the costumed *Belsnickel* who visited each house to see if the children were being good for Christmas. Families of Scandinavian origin also bake their special Christmas cakes, among them hundreds of little peppernuts. The Greek Americans bake *tegenites,* a fried bread made in all manner of shapes. Italian Americans bake Magi cakes, while those of Hungarian ancestry prefer cookies and cakes filled with poppy seeds.

Almost every church and school in the country has a special program to celebrate the Yuletide. Church choirs hold special rehearsals for their programs of sacred music. Most familiar of all Christmas music are the carols that are sung year after year in a custom that has become endeared to the hearts of all. A custom borrowed from the English is observed when groups go forth on Christmas Eve to sing carols. In the stillness of the night their voices ring out with "Silent Night," "O Little Town of Bethlehem" and other familiar carols. Some of the groups stay out all night, their cold vigils broken now and then when they are invited inside at some of the houses for a hot drink and cookies.

Carol singing has become a tradition in certain public places in cities and towns all over the United States. On the lawn of the White House in Washington, D.C., and at Rockefeller Center in New York City, carols are sung around huge Christmas trees. In Wanamaker's store in Philadelphia, carols are sung around the bronze eagle in the Grand Court with the huge pipe organ playing an accompaniment to the voices of the shoppers.

Candlelight services are held all over the nation on Christmas Eve. In most churches this hour of vigil is from eleven until midnight. It is the most sacred time of all the season, for it commemorates the holy Birth, when the Star shone in the East and angels proclaimed glad tidings to the world. The soft glow of candlelight over the church is remindful to all that Christ is the "Light of the World."

In the Moravian Church the candlelight service is called the Christmas Love Feast. Two of these are held on Christmas Eve. The earlier one is especially for the children. The love feast takes place when each child is served with a cup of de-caffeinated coffee and a bun. Following this, while carols are sung, trays of small beeswax candles are passed through the congregation, each candle dressed with its colored paper frill to catch the melting wax. While the twinkling lights of the tiny tapers shed their light over the church, a boy soloist from the choir leads in the antiphonal singing of the Christmas hymn "O Morning Star."

An old and familiar ritual is observed on Christmas Eve in homes all over America: the hanging of the Christmas stocking by the little ones. Though a similar custom is followed in several other countries, nowhere else is there a person to fill the stockings exactly like the one in the United States. Santa Claus is distinctly American in character. In other countries he is almost always the Saint Nicholas of Bishop of Myra fame. But here he is a jolly old man of roly-poly stature with a furred red suit and cap and a big pack on his back. True, the American Santa started as Saint Nicholas long ago in the Dutch colony of New Amsterdam, now New York. But gradually he changed to the character we know today and several things caused this transformation. First of all, there was his name. His original name in the Dutch colony was *San Nicolaas*. When little children said his name fast it sounded like Santa Claus. But how did he change from the stately bishop who wore a mantle and carried a cross, to a fat, bewhiskered countrified-looking man carrying a pack of toys on his back?

The greatest influence in his transformation was " 'Twas the Night Before Christmas," a rollicking poem written by Dr. Clement Moore of New York for his own children in 1822. It was published the following year and was immediately taken to the hearts of boys and girls everywhere.

Around the time of the Civil War, the famous American cartoonist Thomas Nast began to draw pictures of a jolly, bewhiskered Santa Claus in a red, fur-trimmed suit who was shown with a sleigh and reindeer. Gradually the "elf" of the Moore poem grew to normal size in the Nast pictures, and the Santa Claus that we know today became firmly established in everyone's mind. It would be hard for children to recognize him in any other form than that described in " 'Twas the Night Before Christmas":

> He was dressed all in fur from his head to his foot,
> And his clothes were all tarnished with ashes and soot;
> A bundle of toys he had flung on his back,
> And he looked like a pedlar just opening his pack.
>
> His eyes—how they twinkled! his dimples how merry!
> His cheeks were like roses, his nose like a cherry!
> His droll little mouth was drawn up like a bow,
> And the beard of his chin was as white as the snow!

The stump of a pipe he held tight in his teeth,
And the smoke it encircled his head like a wreath;
He had a broad face and a little round belly,
That shook when he laughed like a bowl full of jelly.

CHRISTMAS DAY

We have discussed the many activities that take place in the days before Christmas. What about Christmas Day in the United States, and how is it celebrated?

Through much of the night on the eve of Christmas, many hands have been busy getting last-minute things ready for Christmas Day. At last the lights go off in the houses and the towns lie dark under the stars while children dream of Santa Claus. Then the late dawn breaks and the houses come alive again, with boys and girls rushing to the living room to see the tree and to grab the fat, funny-shaped stockings from the mantelpiece. Eager fingers pull out the packages and

fruit and candy hidden inside and while they are doing this, Mother and Father and older brothers and sisters join the little ones. Gaily wrapped parcels are opened and the room is filled with exclamations of "Oh" and "Thank you" and "See what I got!" It's some time before breakfast is thought of. But finally after everyone is dressed they all sit around the breakfast table still talking about their surprises.

But this is Christmas morning, Christ's Birthday, and in millions of homes the people go to church. There, everyone enjoys the Christmas hymns and the special music by the choir.

Back home again, the next important thing is the big Christmas dinner. Everyone is familiar with the American Christmas dinner menu: turkey and the fixin's, mashed potatoes and turnips, creamed onions, salads, pumpkin and mincemeat pies, fruit cake, nuts and apples!

In most sections of the country, the weather is cold on Christmas Day and, if the children are lucky, there is a white Christmas. This means that the boys and girls can spend the afternoon trying out their new sleds or going to the pond to ice-skate.

The churches in many places hold their Christmas entertainment on Christmas night and this often is the occasion for another kind of White Christmas. Every person attending takes some kind of food to church wrapped in white paper. These packages are placed under the Christmas tree and later distributed to the needy.

Christmas is the time for giving, especially to those who are less fortunate. In every city and town the needy are remembered by religious and social and civic organizations at Christmastime with gifts of food, clothing and fuel. In the large cities there are free Christmas dinners for the poor given at the missions and by the Salvation Army.

There is still another opportunity for giving at Christmas. Every year a Christmas Seal sale is conducted by the National Tuberculosis Association. Annually since 1907 the tiny Christmas seals have gone through the mails into the homes of the American people. Those who buy and use them are helping in the prevention and treatment of tuberculosis and other chest diseases. The seals, used by the millions, have become an American symbol of Christmas.

IN THE EAST

Christmas was not always celebrated in New England. When the Pilgrims and the Puritans came to establish colonies in the New World, they brought with them the strict laws of their church back in England. In 1659 a law was passed in the General Court of Massachusetts making the keeping of Christmas a penal offense. For greeting his neighbor or friend with "A Merry Christmas" one could be fined five shillings.

In the middle eighteen hundreds the Episcopal Sunday schools of New England began to observe Christmas Day. Gradually other church groups presented Christmas programs. By and by, Christmas was recognized as a holiday by the New England states.

Nowadays, if you were to walk down a street in the Beacon Hill section of Boston on Christmas Eve you would not dream that Boston had ever been cool to Christmas.

Wreaths or bright holly branches are hung on every door, while candles gleam at every window. The soft candle glow lights the way for groups of carolers whose voices ring

through the frosty night. It is said that the custom of lighted candles in the window on Christmas Eve came to Boston by way of immigrants from Ireland. In the "old country" it was important on Christmas Eve to place a lighted candle in the window to light the Christ Child on His way.

Rockefeller Center in New York City is the dazzling background each year for a huge Christmas tree. It is said that this tree, always impressively decorated, is viewed by more people than any other Christmas tree in the world. Crowds gather about it not only to enjoy its beauty but to hear the carol concerts by the Radio Center Choristers. Visitors to New York at Christmastime are irresistibly drawn to this spot where the great illumined tree, the lights gleaming from windows of the tall buildings surrounding it, and the bright figures of skaters on the ice at the Center leave an unforget-table impression.

Pennsylvania has its own Christmas City. Thousands of persons visit Bethlehem, Pennsylvania, during Christmas week each year, where they are greeted by the sight of an immense star, ninety-one feet high, erected on South Moun-tain above the city. On the Hill-to-Hill Bridge stands a giant Christmas tree constructed from one hundred and fifty spruce trees, beautifully illumined with hundreds of electric lights. Bethlehem is the home of the Moravians who are noted for their Christmas customs. Prominent in their observance is the *putz* (the German word for ornament), a lovingly planned and carefully detailed Nativity scene, in which Moravian families proudly display the beautifully carved figurines they have saved for generations. Some of these scenes take up an entire room and the many-pointed Mora-vian star is always suspended from the ceiling above them. When visitors come to see the *putz,* the mother of the house-hold recites the Bible story of the first Christmas.

IN THE SOUTH

Many years ago the French settlers brought a Christmas custom to Louisiana that was unique in this country. It was the custom of "shooting in" Christmas with fireworks, fire-arms and anything else that would make a loud noise. This noisy way of greeting Christmas Day spread to other states in the South. Today the sale and use of fireworks is banned in the cities but in some rural places one can still hear fire-works booming at midnight to usher in Christmas.

In the olden days, on many of the plantations, Christmas was celebrated in the old English way with many visitors to be entertained over the holidays. Yule logs and wassail bowls were prominent in the celebration. The Yule log was

chosen with care. Usually it was a log that was well water-soaked to ensure that it would burn for many days. There was so much to be done to prepare the vast amount of food for the holidays that most households started on this work right after Thanksgiving. Some idea of the size of the cakes that were baked on the big plantations in those days may be had from the recipe for Martha Washington's Christmas cake which, among other ingredients, called for forty eggs.

IN THE MIDWEST

The people of Scandinavian descent in our midwestern states, Minnesota, Wisconsin, North Dakota and Illinois, observe Christmas with some of the customs brought here from their native land. One of these is the feeding of the birds on Christmas Day. The householder erects a tall pole in the yard and fastens a large sheaf of grain at the top. This is always the finest sheaf of wheat, barley or oats, saved from threshing time in the fall.

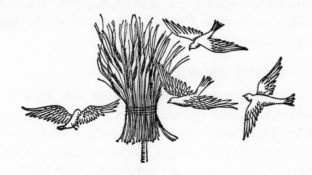

IN THE SOUTHWEST

The custom of enacting the Posadas came to certain border states from Mexico and is observed religiously for the nine nights preceding Christmas by every Spanish-speaking family. The Posadas are described in this book in the chapter on Mexico.

In some places in Texas and New Mexico, a very old Christmas drama called *Los Pastores* (The Shepherds) is given. Sometimes this is enacted every night through the period from Christmas to Candlemas, February second. One part of the play depicts the struggle between Good, usually portrayed by an old man with a white beard carrying a cross, and Evil, enacted by Lucifer and six other devils. The devils try to prevent the shepherds from approaching the manger to worship the Infant Jesus. At the end of the play,

Good overcomes Evil and the shepherds finally come before the Child—a doll laid upon the lowest step of the altar— and bestow a kiss upon Him.

A *Misa de Gallo,* or Mass of the Cockcrow, is celebrated at midnight in Roman Catholic Churches in the Spanish-speaking sections of the Southwest.

AMONG THE AMERICAN INDIANS

At the Salt River Indian Reservation near Phoenix, Arizona, where the Pima Indians live, Christmas Eve is a very busy time. Those who are to sing at the Christmas service in the church next day are practicing the carols and Christmas hymns while women are preparing food for the feast. On Christmas morning the people gather for miles around to attend the church service and to eat the good dinner. That evening there is a special program in the church, after which Santa Claus distributes gifts and candy. It is a day of all days for the Pimas, one looked forward to all year.

In the pueblos of New Mexico, the Indians light their villages at Christmastime with *luminarias.* These are a unique kind of lantern made of colored paper bags half-filled with sand and holding lighted candles. They are ranged along the walls, on the rooftops and in lines along the hillsides a few feet apart, and the night is transformed into a fairyland of soft gleaming lights. Small bonfires add to the unforgettable effect.

In their churches the Indians view Nativity Plays on Christmas Eve, after which they are entertained by dancers dressed in their native costumes. To the chant of a chorus and the beat of their drums, the dancers perform the Deer Dance, the favorite for Christmas Eve.

After church, the Indians form a procession dressed in their gayest costumes. They carry *achones,* torches of burning cedar or pine, and are always preceded by the person who carries a statue of the Virgin Mary dressed in ornamental robes. As the people march they chant in their native tongue.

IN THE WEST

Fifty-four miles from Sanger, California, is America's National Christmas Tree. This tree, known as the General Grant, is said to be the oldest living thing on earth. At the time of Jesus's birth in Nazareth, it had already attained the age of two thousand years. The magnificent sequoia is 267 feet high and has a circumference of 107 feet. On Christmas Day in 1926 it was formally dedicated as the Nation's Christmas Tree. Annually ever since, it has been visited by thousands who go there every year to attend a worship service on the Sunday before Christmas.

While almost every town in the United States has its special community Christmas tree to celebrate the season, the town of Altadena in California can boast of a "mile of Christmas trees." People travel there to see a long lane of huge deodar cedars trimmed with colored electric lights. The trees were planted long ago by Frederick J. Woodbury. While traveling in India, he had admired the graceful native cedars and decided to plant seeds on his ranch to grow them. That was in 1882. Now, the ranch lane bordered by two hundred trees is a street in Altadena. The tall trees, noted for their graceful Oriental beauty, attract thousands of visitors who drive their cars down the brightly illumined avenue to enjoy the unusual sight.

Each year on the streets of Santa Barbara, California, a group of carolers go about, dressed, like the old English "waits," in long red capes and pointed caps.

High on the mountain of Flagstaff in Colorado, a Christmas star two hundred fifty feet tall can be seen for miles. Below the mountain is the city of Boulder, where a prolonged celebration takes place. It begins on the first Saturday in December with the arrival of Santa Claus, who presents small gifts to the children assembled for the occasion. It ends on Twelfth Night when all the Christmas trees of the town are burnt together in one tremendous bonfire.

A Yule Log Hunt has taken place annually since 1933 at Palmer Lake, Colorado. This celebration is unique in the United States. A tree chosen for the Yule Log is cut down and then carefully hidden. Those who join in the Hunt at Christmastime all wear capes and hoods of red or green to represent the people of old England in the days when choosing a Yule log was an important feature of the Christmas celebration. Then, again following the English custom, the log is dragged into town with great ceremony, with the person who has found it riding upon it triumphantly.

IN ALASKA

Our forty-ninth state might well be considered by some as the home of Santa Claus, with its cold climate and snow sufficient to please his "eight tiny reindeer." In thousands of homes in Alaska, Christmas is celebrated much as it is in the rest of the United States, with children hanging up their stockings and everybody eating a big dinner. There, however, roast venison may sometimes be substituted for turkey.

Alaskans who belong to the Greek Orthodox Church maintain a custom that is great fun for the children. Each evening during Christmas week a procession takes place, called "Carrying the Star." The star, covered with colored paper and mounted on a pole, is carried about the streets by a star-bearer, while two other boys carry lanterns on a pole. The men, women and children who follow the star-bearers are sometimes invited into the homes for refreshments. But the exciting part of the ceremony comes after the second night when the star-bearers are chased by "Herod's men," men and boys wearing all sorts of odd clothing. Originally, this little play-acting was to represent Herod's soldiers trying to destroy the children of Bethlehem. But now for all who take part in the chase there is only the fun of the game.

IN HAWAII

In startling contrast with the climate of Alaska are the sunny, warm days of a Hawaiian Christmas. The boys and girls of our fiftieth state can only imagine what a snowy Christmas would be like. They often eat their Christmas dinner out-of-doors. Afterward, they take part in sports and games.

Christmas was proclaimed a holiday in Hawaii in 1862 by King Kamehameha IV. That same year the first candle-light service was held. Today the Nativity scene is much in evidence in Hawaiian stores and at church and civic gatherings. Christmas carols have been sung with great enthusiasm ever since 1823 when an American missionary, Reverend Hiram Bingham, translated "Joy to the World" for the Islanders.

Evergreens do not grow in the Islands but every year thousands of Christmas trees are transported by ship from the Pacific Northwest. Often the trees are painted white to simulate the snow-covered trees Hawaiian children have never seen. They are trimmed with balls and tinsel just as on the mainland, but Hawaiian *leis* made of shells, nuts and flowers are added, too.

The Hawaiian greeting for "Merry Christmas!" is *"Mele*

Kalikimaha!" But this is only one of the many forms of greeting, for Hawaiian citizens are of many races and tongues. They live on their beloved Islands in harmony, and at no time is this more apparent than at the holy season of Christmas when all unite in celebrating the birth of the Infant Jesus.

IN PUERTO RICO

Christmas celebrations in Puerto Rico last for a long time. Three Kings' Day is observed January 6th. The Three Kings, represented by children dressed in appropriate costumes of the Biblical kings, go from house to house presenting gifts. They are followed by a procession of angels and shepherds carrying garlands of flowers.

The girls and boys of Puerto Rico fill boxes with grass and set them on the roof for the camels of the Magi (Wise Men). Next morning when they examine the boxes they find that the grass is gone and gifts have been left in them instead. In their country, instead of Santa Claus, it is the Magi who are said to leap across the rooftops to bring the presents.

ELIZABETH HOUGH SECHRIST

CANADA

Christmas on the Gaspé

ALL THE MORNING, ON THE DAY BEFORE CHRISTMAS, THE
house was filled with excitement and bustle. The kitchen was
full of many good smells, for Tante Eugénie was baking all
kinds of things. For the past two weeks she had been baking
cookies and cakes, and several crocks full stood on the shelf.

The rabbits were dressed and cleaned ready for the
réveillon ragout. The pea soup was bubbling on the back
of the stove all ready for supper. The lovely tree stood in
its corner of the parlor with the angel at the top, and candles
on the tips of the branches ready to be lighted. All the house
was shining clean.

Suzanne, Tante Eugénie and Berthe were dressed in their

36

best waiting for Uncle Jacques and André to be ready. Cippy and Paule were scrubbed and dressed, Cippy's hair in little damp curls and Paule's tied back with a ribbon. It seemed like Sunday, but of course it wasn't! It was almost Christmas Eve! Pretty soon, Uncle Jacques called in the door and they all went to church for confession before Midnight Mass.

When they came back, each one brought to Tante Eugénie their gifts for the tree from their hiding places. Such mystery! Such tiptoeing! Suzanne saw Uncle Jacques come out of the door to the parlor, and close it quickly behind him. She heard a rustle of paper and saw Tante Eugénie slip something behind her as she closed the door to the little cupboard under the stairs. André kept something under his coat until he got past the kitchen, then he gave it to Tante, who opened the door just a crack. They whispered for a moment, then the door was shut again. It was hard to keep Cippy and Paule from seeing. They were all eyes and ears, and so excited they couldn't keep still. Every time the parlor door opened they craned their necks to see.

"Va-t'en! Va-t'en!"—Go away! Tante Eugénie scolded. Then they would be good for a few minutes, and turn somersaults all over the kitchen. They nearly squashed Pouf, so he took refuge under the stove.

Suzanne brought downstairs the gifts she had, and whispered to Uncle Jacques to put them on the tree for her. She didn't want Tante Eugénie to even *see* the package that smelled like perfume. She had wrapped the scarf in a piece of red tissue that Mr. Ryan had given her, and had written a name carefully on each package. Pepère sat quietly by the stove smoking his pipe. He didn't seem very much excited, but he looked happy.

Tante Eugénie kept going back and forth, into the kitchen, up the stairs, into the little cupboard, even down to the cellar. What *could* be down there! Cippy and Paule got down on their hands and knees to look when the trap door was open but they couldn't see, and when Tante came up she kept whatever it was under her apron.

It seemed to Suzanne that the time would *never* come for the tree and the réveillon. She got out her pencil and tablet, and began to draw a picture of the tree. She wished again she had some paints like the tourist lady had. The colors would be so lovely on her picture.

It was dark before Tante Eugénie and Uncle Jacques had everything ready. Since the day before Christmas is a fast day, there was only pea soup for supper. The little ones must say their prayers and go to bed to rest until time for the Midnight Mass. Suzanne thought she never could go to sleep, but she was soon deep in dreams.

She was wakened by Berthe, who took her hand and whispered so as not to wake Cippy and Paule. They were too small to go and Pepère is too old, so he stayed at home with them.

They must all wrap up well; it was cold. Suzanne wished she hadn't lost her mittens, but the old one of Berthe's was better than none, and she would walk beside Uncle Jacques and put her hand in his.

As they turned out of the lane, people were coming from

farther down the road, crunching along in the snow, the frosty air making their voices sound close.

"*Joyeux Noël!*" Merry Christmas! they called as they passed. "Noël, Noël!" The church bells began to ring. Suzanne shivered with excitement and looked up at the stars that filled the sky. One star looked especially bright. It looked as if it stood right over the church, and Suzanne thought it *might* be the Star of Bethlehem!

"So," said Uncle Jacques, as he squeezed her hand, "it is Noël! You are 'appy, eh, Ti-Su?" He swept her along beside him, her feet scarcely touching the ground.

"Oh, oui!" Suzanne laughed back at him, and skipped as much as she *could* skip with the heavy boots on her feet.

All along the way to the church, dark figures joined them from each lane and gateway. From each one came the greeting, "Joyeux Noël! Joyeux Noël!"

The church looked beautiful. The pillars were wrapped with greens, there were branches of evergreen on the window sills, and a tall pine tree stood at each side of the altar. Soft candlelight showed the gilt edge on the Virgin's blue robe, reflected in the gold altar service, lighted the figure of a saint, and made real the little carved figures of the crèche at the left of the altar. The shepherds were kneeling in real straw, the Ste. Vierge was sitting on a *real* little wooden bench, and the tiny Christ Child was lying in a *real* little manger made of wood. Suzanne could see it all very plainly from where she was sitting. Softly, the choir began to sing "Adeste Fideles." Then the altar boys, two by two, with lighted candles, came slowly down the aisle. The tiny ones first, Etienne and little Jean, then Paul and Leonard and the others, the older ones next, and then the big boys like André and Jules. They looked very solemn, and hardly like the same boys that played so roughly every day.

After the service, Tante Eugénie invited Ol' Batees' to come home with them to the réveillon. He was glad to come and said he would bring his fiddle.

Such laughing and talking! Such a shouting of "Happy Christmas!" Everyone was in a good humor, everyone seemed very happy.

It didn't take long for Tante Eugénie to get the supper on the table. Uncle Jacques got out the jug of home-made wine and Ol' Batees' got out his fiddle.

Suzanne and André and Berthe danced around the kitchen. "Ol' Batees', he dance too," he said, his thick boots clumping on the floor.

The fire in the stove was snapping and cracking, the tea-kettle was humming, the fiddle was singing under Ol' Batees' fingers, the children were laughing and dancing.

Then Tante Eugénie called them all to the table. All was quiet for a moment while they blessed themselves, then all broke into happy cries of "Joyeux Noël!" as they sat down to the feast.

Then came the time for the gifts. Suzanne's throat ached with excitement. Cippy and Paule were standing at the door of the parlor, waiting for Uncle Jacques to carry in the lamp and to light the candles on the tree. At last he threw open the door. There stood the beautiful tree with little packages tied all over it, and at the base! Oh, Suzanne just couldn't believe her eyes! She sat down on the floor with the other children, in front of Pepère and Tante Eugénie. Uncle Jacques was to hand out the gifts.

"Aha!" he said, "here is somet'ing for good little girls." To Cippy he gave a cradle and to Paule a small cart. There were warm socks for Uncle Jacques, for Pepère, and for André, that Tante Eugénie had knitted, a dress for Berthe that Tante Eugénie had made from one of her own. Then Uncle Jacques picked up and hid behind him what Suzanne had seen peeking out from under the tree. She saw Uncle Jacques' eyes twinkle as he looked at her.

"So," he said, "now de pe ti' Suzanne can go, vite! vite! over de snow." And he gave her the most beautiful pair of snowshoes she had ever seen. She was so happy she hugged them to her and didn't say a word, but put them down long enough to throw her arms around Uncle Jacques as far as they would go.

Next, came a pair of skis for André. "So, *that* is why there were always wood splinters on the floor in the mornings!" André was as delighted as Ti-Su.

Suzanne held her breath while André unwrapped the scarf. She wanted to see what Tante Eugénie would say, too, when she saw it.

"I made it all myself!" she said as André's eyes opened in surprise.

"Tch! Tch!" said Tante, *"you* mak' de weave?" She held up the scarf and shook her head. "Eet is beautiful!"

Then Ol' Batees' said, " 'Ere ees somet'ing soft for de

little Suzanne," and threw it into her lap. She undid the wrapping with fingers that trembled. Oh, that good Tante Eugénie! She had knitted a new pair of red mittens for Suzanne. *That* was what she had been hiding in the little cupboard under the stairs for such a long time.

Then Uncle Jacques reached up and took off the tree the little package Suzanne had bought for Tante Eugénie.

"Umm," he said, "it smell good. Gif' for a lady!" And he gave it to Tante Eugénie. Suzanne could hardly wait till she took off the red string and undid the paper. Maybe she wouldn't like it. But how could she help it? It was so sweet. Tante Eugénie took off the last scrap of paper and what do you think it was? *A little Cupid made of soap!* Tante

Eugénie *did* like it, even if her eyes were filled with tears. Grownups don't usually get presents. Then Uncle Jacques handed to Suzanne the package from the United States. Everyone watched to see what was in that package! Suzanne opened it. A card dropped out: "For Ti-Su who would love to paint!" And there was a box of beautiful water colors and brushes from the tourist lady!

The candles were burning low and all the gifts had been taken from the tree. It was almost morning, and Cippy was yawning. Paule was asleep against Berthe's shoulder, Pepère was nodding in his chair, and Tante Eugénie could hardly keep her eyes open.

Ol' Batees' said, "Merci! madame, for de good réveillon," and once again he said, "Joyeux Noël!" and left.

What a happy time it had been. André went up to the loft, and all the children went up the stairs to bed, with Berthe to help them. Suzanne didn't even notice the long shadows up the wall; she knew that the strange bundle on the chair was only Tante Eugénie's old dress, that the moaning sound she heard was only the wind in the sycamore tree.

She heard the sleepy murmuring of Cippy and Paule as they said their prayers for Berthe. She said her own and crept into bed. She sighed with happiness at the thought of the snowshoes and the mittens and the beautiful paints; of how André had loved the scarf she had made him; of how Tante Eugénie loved the sweet little soap baby; and of how Uncle Jacques would enjoy the tobacco. She opened her eyes once more, and there, shining in her window, was the bright star. It shone softly and seemed to say, "Joyeux Noël, Joyeux Noël."

MARGUERITE DE ANGELI

MEXICO

Christmas in Mexico

CHRISTMAS COMES BUT ONCE A YEAR BUT THE MEXICANS make the most of it. Probably nowhere else in the world is Christmas celebrated so thoroughly and with so much color as in Mexico. In the Mexican observance there is a happy mingling of the religious with the social, and this spirit of festivity and reverence is shared by·all.

The children of Mexico have several weeks to revel in the delights of Christmas, for its celebration starts on the sixteenth of December and ends with observance of the Epiphany, January sixth. No doubt some of our American children would like to adopt the Mexican Christmas because of the long time they would have to celebrate, and yet it is so different from our own Christmas that we should probably not want to give up those things which make our Yuletide so dear to us. I wonder how many girls and boys would be willing to give up Santa Claus and their Christmas tree for the things that are important in the observance of Christmas in Mexico. Let us see what Mexico has to offer in those three weeks of celebration.

About two weeks before Christmas the market places begin to display their Christmas wares, but before that time if we were to go to the small Indian villages in the mountains beyond the city we might see a veritable Santa Claus shop in each adobe house. Every member of the Indian family is gathered together, fingers flying busily, eyes bright and voices raised in song over the joy they feel in the making of the Christmas toys. Everyone, from the tiniest child to the aged grandparents, shares in the work. The tiny ones are learning just as the aged ones have learned many years before, to make the trinkets and toys that will bring pesos to their pockets at the Christmas *puestos*. They cut and carve and paint, they mix and mold clay, do exquisite work in leather, weave baskets of reed and willow, and create objects of beauty as only they can do. Then at last just before the time when Mexico begins the universal celebration of the Posadas, these workers pack their treasures in large baskets, pile their whole families into donkey carts or automobiles, and go to the cities to sell their wares.

In every city the *puestos* or market-stalls spring up. In Mexico City the Alameda is lined on both sides with them.

The merchants have looked forward to this time. The Indian families have come from their homes in the mountains to add to the colorful scene of the Christmas season. The Indians stick poles into the ground and erect their booths by hanging gay-colored blankets on three sides. Across the front of their stalls they string wires from which the bright *piñatas* hang. (We shall hear more about the *piñata* later.) What a wealth of objects these Christmas *puestos* flaunt before us! One would need to be hardened indeed to be able to resist them. Objects made of clay in every size and shape, artistic blue glassware, all kinds of baskets, toys and trinkets, and cunning Indian dolls; all these and many more we see in the Indian stalls. From small *puestos* are being sold a wonderful assortment of sweetmeats: candies and nuts, cakes made of *ajonjoli* seed, cheeses, thin red peppers, figs, dates and other dried fruits, and sweet preserved bananas. Then there are the rag dolls! A baby without a rag doll in Mexico would be like a Santa without a beard! Whole booths are given over to the display of these dolls, black, white and Indian, and street vendors are constantly urging us to buy them. A family must be poor indeed not to buy at least one of them against the gift-giving time of Epiphany. A display of tiny waxen and clay figures of the Holy Family remind us of the Posadas. People are buying figures of Mary and Joseph and the Holy Child, the shepherds (*pastores*), the Magi, and even the little donkey on which Mary rode into Bethlehem. Great mounds of green moss and pampas plumes are sold for decoration. Evergreens are sold too, but these are used more in the decorating of churches. Girls wearing gay shawls are selling flowers from their heaped-up baskets. Men with poles across their shoulders from which the always conspicuous *piñatas* are suspended chant the merits of these gay-colored objects. Everywhere there are people with huge baskets, women with small

babies on their backs, Indians squatting silently beside their wares, Mexican merchants shouting and bartering, beautiful *señoras* bargaining with the peddlers, happy children running here and there, and a festive confusion reigning over all.

On the night of December 16th the celebration of the Posadas begins and continues for nine nights, the last being observed on Christmas Eve. The name comes from the word *posada* meaning inn or lodging-house, and the significance of course is the inn at Bethlehem, Judea, in the story of the Nativity. The Posadas are still celebrated in certain parts of Spain. The custom came to Mexico from Spain many years ago.

There are two ways of observing the Posadas in Mexico. In many places nine families combine in the celebration, meeting at a different one of the nine houses each night. The

grandest celebration comes on Christmas Eve, and the
largest home is usually chosen for the Christmas Eve Posada.
The second way is to have the Posadas celebrated in the
same house all nine nights, with only the family present.
The first, however, is the more popular way, and thus the
time has come to be one of great social activity and entertaining. The Mexican women plan their costumes carefully,
and try to wear a different gown on each of the nine nights.
The Christmas season is courting season, and it is not
unusual for a courtship during the Posadas to end in an en-
gagement of marriage.

The Posadas begin with the recitation of the rosary led by
the head of the house. Then family, guests and servants
carry lighted candles and form a procession which marches
about the house. The procession is led by two children carrying images of Mary and Joseph. The figures are dressed
in satin and lace, having been given all the grandeur that
these people can bestow upon them. As the people in the
procession move from room to room they chant the Litany
of Loretto, a special prayer. At the door of each room they
stop and beg for admittance for the weary pilgrims, St. Joseph and the Virgin Mary. But at each door they are refused
admittance. At last, however, they come to a room where an
altar has previously been erected. At the door of this room
they are permitted to enter. Here is an altar representing
the scene of the Nativity: a hillside decorated with moss and
green branches, a stable with an empty manger, shepherds
and sheep, trees and houses—all in miniature. The figures of
Mary and Joseph are placed in the stable. The manger in

the stable remains empty until the ninth night of the Posadas, on Christmas Eve.

The first part of the Posada is strictly a religious enactment. Then comes the social part. When the procession is over and the prayer at the altar has been said, the party is invited to the patio of the house for the breaking of the *piñata*. This is the ceremony which has been eagerly awaited by all the children. Here, in the courtyard or the patio, hangs the *piñata* in all its colorfulness. It is the gayest of the gay, with brightly colored tissue-paper streamers and glittering tinsel adorning it. It may be almost any shape one could think of, for the variety and assortment of *piñatas* sold in the market places are almost innumerable. It may be in the shape of a bird, a fish, a doll, a fat little woman with flounced petticoats, a fat little man with a round fat belly, a ship, a shoe, a house, a horse, or just a jolly, gay bowl of pottery. That is what all *piñatas* really are, earthenware bowls in disguise. Now the children, one by one, are blindfolded and led close to the *piñata,* given a stick, and allowed three whacks each at the bowl. It is great fun, for of course, being blindfolded, the children will not have very good aim, and often the blows simply fall upon the air. At last, however, the *piñata* receives the blow that does the trick—knocks it to pieces—and what a scramble follows! The contents of the *piñata* are scattered about the floor, and the children and even the grown people fall upon them eagerly, for inside it were all sorts of sweetmeats, whistles, cute little figures and funny toys.

On each of the nine nights, the Posadas are observed with

a religious procession and the merry ending—the breaking of the *piñata*. But it is on the last night of all, Christmas Eve, that the most important ceremony takes place. The Posada, as on the eight previous nights, begins with the procession. This time, one of the little girls leading the procession carries the image of the Infant Jesus in her arms. When all rooms have been visited, when the Virgin and St. Joseph have been refused admittance and then finally admitted to the room where the altar is—then comes the important part of the nine nights' ceremony. The procession kneels before the altar—the scene of the blessed nativity—and the father of the household offers up a prayer. Then, while a hymn is being chanted, the father takes the Holy Child from the one who is carrying it and places it in the cradle or manger, which for eight nights has remained empty. Tonight is the birthday of the Infant. He is placed in the cradle, and a hymn is sung to the Holy Babe. "Alleluia, alleluia! Let us rejoice because the Lord has deigned to come to His people! Let us sing praises to the Lord. Come ye, sing and rejoice! Blessed is He that cometh in the name of the Lord. Hosanna in the Highest!"

After this ceremony the party goes once more to the patio. Tonight it is gaily decorated with lighted lanterns and many flowers. The festivities begin with an exciting display of fireworks, and soon everyone is in gay spirits with the breaking of the elaborate *piñata*. There is much singing and dancing, fun and laughter. But all this is interrupted for attendance of Midnight Mass at the church. Then the dancing and music continue, and keep up well into dawn.

In many parts of Mexico, Christmas Eve is celebrated with the picturesque *Pastores,* especially in the villages of the nation. From the house of the maestro, or singing master, comes the sound of the sweet voices of his boys. They come up the street amid a blaze of light. They carry staffs of bells and many of them bear poles with lighted stars or crescents shining at the top. The stars are made of tissue-paper, and in the center of each, a candle burns. The procession of boys marches to the church, where all night long their voices can be heard singing and chanting while people come and go.

Christmas Day is very quiet, compared with the season before it. It is a time of friendly greeting and visiting, but no gifts are exchanged. The house is always trimmed with beautiful flowers, and this even in the poorer districts of Mexican cities, for flowers are very cheap. The beautiful *Noche Bueno,* a scarlet Christmas plant, is seen in great profusion. One of the most gorgeous of the Christmas plants is the Flame Leaf, or poinsettia, as we know it, which grows to a height of ten feet, and has brilliant red bracts with a yellow flower in the center, and rich green stem and leaves. When the plants are seen growing they are breathtaking. This Christmas plant was named for Joel Robert Poinsett, prime minister to Mexico from 1825 to 1829, who introduced it to America.

Christmas Day in Mexico might well be mistaken for a day in our late spring or early summer. From the garden in the patio comes the scent of roses and heliotrope, and the soft breezes that are wafted through the windows as we eat our Mexican Christmas dinner make us eager to be out-of-doors where we can enjoy the delightful weather.

But the Christmas dinner is a work of culinary art, and the *señora* who has gathered her family and special friends about her table has spent much thought upon it. Skilled Indian women have been busy for days getting ready the Mexican dishes with great care and artfulness. Fascinating dishes appear on the table. One of these is the *Ensalada de la Noche Buena*. It consists of a mixture of many fruits and vegetables, and is garnished with gay-colored candies. Roast turkey is served, too, with tortillas and fried peppers. Both chocolate and coffee are served as beverages. The Mexican *chocolatl* was first made by the Aztecs and is a favorite drink among the people. The coffee looks very strong as it is brought to the table. It looks like syrup. And that is exactly what it is, for the Mexicans prepare their coffee by making an extract. After a portion of the coffee extract is poured into each cup, boiled milk is added. Champagne is sometimes served at this elaborate meal, and souvenirs are given to the guests.

Santa Claus is almost unknown in Mexico, but in his place many of the Mexican children, and especially the little Indian boys and girls, know of the kindly old Aztec god of the sun, *Quetzalcoatl*. He has been pictured as an old man with a long white beard and flowing white robes, and is a most beneficent old gentleman. He was supposed to have taught the art of civilized living to the ancient Aztecs and, being god of the sun, he was also responsible for the beauty of the Christmas season. By his favor, the Indians believed, the world became abundant with fruit and flowers and verdant with the growth of the springtime.

Mexican children write letters to the Christ Child before Epiphany, listing the toys and other gifts their hearts crave. And having that same faith with which the American children hang up their stockings on Christmas Eve, the Mexican boys and girls place their shoes at the foot of their beds on January fifth, the Eve of Epiphany. If there is a balcony on the house where several children live, one may see a row of small shoes waiting for the gifts of the three Magi as they pass through the village or city on their legendary visit to the Holy City to behold the Christ Child.

There are masses and elaborate services in all the churches at Epiphany, with beautiful music, thousands of lighted candles, and burning incense to add to the expression of religious joy.

Christmas in Mexico! Music, lights, dancing, singing, fun and laughter over the *piñatas,* gifts from the Magi found in the children's shoes on the morn of Epiphany, love and devotional services for the Infant Jesus in the ceremony of the Posadas, and reverence and music in the Churches— this is what Christmas means to the Mexicans. We can understand with what joyful anticipation all the people of Mexico look forward to this season.

ELIZABETH HOUGH SECHRIST

SOUTH AMERICA

Christmas in South America

POSADAS LIKE THOSE IN SPAIN AND MEXICO ARE POPULAR IN South American Countries. They begin on December sixteenth and end on Christmas Eve. The beginning of the Posadas is the time for writing notes to the Christ Child. The children put their notes beside the Holy Manger in their *Nacimiento*. Their parents tell them that if they are good, angels will take the notes up to Heaven and deliver them to the Infant Jesus.

Christmas in South America, as far as the weather is concerned, is like our Fourth of July. The stores display gifts for shoppers in the large cities, but it seems entirely too warm to take Christmas shopping seriously. There are ice stalls along the streets in Argentina, Brazil, Chile and Peru. They attract crowds of people. In fact, they seem to be the center of interest, for everyone is anxious to keep as cool as possible.

In Lima, Peru, the markets are crowded on Christmas Day. The Indian merchants have toys, trinkets and all sorts of good things to eat spread out on straw mats on the ground. The good-natured throngs mill around, the people looking the things over and purchasing what they like. It is a very gay crowd. People are jostling, pushing, laughing, and singing to the music of castanets and guitars. Indians are making their way gracefully through the crowds with ice-pails on their heads calling: *"Helado! Helado!"* Cathedral bells call the people to Christmas services. On Christmas Eve when the Cathedral bell rings the people drop to their knees in prayer, and when they rise at the last stroke of the bell they wish each other a *Noche Buena*. On this night the crowds hurry to Cristobel Hill where a cross is erected and blessed by the Archbishop. In Peru the Christmas celebrations are a mingling of the Spanish with those of the Incas, though the more significant of the customs are Spanish.

In Chile on Christmas the Indians hold a grand fiesta. It is much like the county fair that comes in the fall of the year in our own country. The horse races are the main feature of the fiesta, and the Chileans look forward to them all year. The Chilean Indians, who are excellent riders, all come to the fair on horseback. They ride all over the place. Their horses are graceful, beautiful creatures, full of fire.

The celebrations last from early morning until nightfall, and even after, for when night comes there is dancing and singing. By the light of the campfires the sleek Indian braves and the shiny-haired Indian maidens dance to the sound of guitars. Indian costumes and American dress

are mingled. Travelers who happen to attend this Indian fiesta are interested in the booths where beautiful Indian workmanship is displayed in the rugs, blankets and hand-wrought jewelry.

In Andacollo, Chile, there is a statue of the Virgin known as the Virgin del Rosario that is visited by thousands of people every Christmas. She is said to have been dug up by a woodcutter named Collo who was directed to her by a vision.

In Brazil, "Santa Claus" is little known. Those who wait for the jolly fellow call him Papa Noël. They know nothing of a sleigh pulled by eight tiny reindeer, for in Brazil the weather is too warm for sleighs and reindeer. The children expect Papa Noël to come through the window to fill their shoes with gifts. The chimneys, if there are any, are much too small for his entrance. The very hottest season of the year comes to Brazil with Christmas.

In the Argentine, too, the Christmas season is very warm. The day is celebrated very quietly with religious services taking up most of the day. New Year's Day is more important to the grown people than Christmas Day. There is more celebrating then and exchanging of gifts. On the Eve of *Dia de los Reyes,* January sixth, the children place their shoes by the bed with the hope that they will find them filled with gifts in the morning. And they are never disappointed, for the parents of the little Argentines are very generous with their children. A custom which the children never fail to carry out is to leave water and hay outside the door so that the horses of the Three Magi will find a meal to refresh them as they journey toward the Christ Child in the city of Jerusalem.

ELIZABETH HOUGH SECHRIST

ENGLAND

An English Christmas

IT WAS CHRISTMAS VACATION TIME, AND IN A GIRLS' BOARD-ing school in England two girls were saying good-bye. Anne Seymour was a typical English girl of fourteen, eager to get home to her family for the two weeks' holiday. Virginia Lewis, also fourteen, was an American girl who was spending her first year in England. She had fallen in love with the English boarding school that she attended, and the happy, healthy girls who were her classmates, especially Anne.

"Anne, I don't see how I am going to get along without you these two weeks!" she told her friend, pressing Anne's hand in her shy, affectionate manner.

"But, Virginia! You are going to join your family, see your twin and your father and mother! And spend Christmas in Paris. Why, I'd give anything to spend Christmas in Paris. I've always dreamed of it!"

"Yes, but I'd rather just be going home for Christmas," Virginia answered. "And I *shall* miss you dreadfully."

"I'll miss you, too." But Anne's mind was filled with thoughts of home, her parents, her sister Edith, and her two small brothers. She was as homesick this year as usual, in spite of the close friendship she had made.

Last words of good-bye were being said when the girls were interrupted by a messenger who carried a telegram for Miss Virginia Lewis. Anne started to leave the room but stopped at Virginia's "Wait, please."

Then after Virginia had torn the message open and read it, she turned a gloomy face toward her friend.

"Oh, Anne," she said, "this will change everything! Grandmother is very ill. Mother and Dad are leaving at once."

"I am *so* sorry, Virginia," said Anne sympathetically.

"I will just have time to get to London to see them before they leave. Bob and I are to stay in London with Colonel Dare until they return, or, I suppose, until we return to school." There were tears in her eyes as she added, "And everything will be so dull."

"Why, no, it shan't at all!" And Anne suddenly began to dance her friend around the room. "I know just the thing! You and Bob shall spend Christmas with us. Oh, won't it be just too jolly?"

"But, Anne!"

"Nothing of the sort! It is all settled. I had already spoken of it in a letter to Mother when you told me your family had decided to take you to Paris. But now we can all be together!"

And that is what happened to give Virginia and Bob Lewis a real English Christmas that they would not have had otherwise.

When Mrs. Seymour learned that the children were to be separated from their parents at Christmas, she telephoned to the London hotel where the Lewises were staying and asked to have Virginia and Bob spend the Christmas holidays with them at Hayward's Heath. It was a happy arrangement, for the Americans were leaving at once for Liverpool where they would take the boat for New York. Mrs. Seymour would come to London the next day, accompanied by Anne and Edith, and take the children home with her.

But first, before they were to leave London, the five of them were to go on a shopping expedition! Mrs. Seymour, each year just before Christmas, made two special trips to London; one with her two little sons, the other with Anne and Edith.

The morning of the Seymour girls' trip to London dawned bright and clear. The little boys walked over to the station with them, or, rather, they ran, for the little boys never walked. They were a jolly crowd. Edith, who was sixteen, had also just returned from boarding school. She and Anne were chattering like magpies. And their lovely young mother asked question after question. It always seemed as if they could never get everything said during these holidays, and so they wasted no time in silence.

The little boys were kissed good-bye and told to be good, for their turn for London would come in a few days; and then the three boarded the train and were off. The hour's ride to London passed pleasantly. In a short time they found themselves at the hotel where the Lewis children were waiting for them.

Everyone was introduced all around, and then Mrs. Seymour told them what her plans for the day were. She was a wonderful mother, full of ideas for the happiness of her children. Each year this trip to London was made a great event; she wanted to have them enjoy it to the utmost. Their little guests had never seen London at Christmas time, so that the day would be doubly interesting to them.

And what a day it was! There was just time enough before luncheon to go shopping. Virginia and Bob found the shops quite as crowded, as interesting and as much decorated as those of New York. There was one difference, however. People in London were not in so much of a hurry as in New York!

It took them longer than they intended to make all the purchases they needed, so it was nearly two o'clock when they went back to the hotel for luncheon. The two hours between luncheon and train time were spent doing a number of interesting things. When the five of them were at last settled on the train and speeding homeward to Hayward's Heath, Anne leaned back in her seat and sighed deeply.

"Oh," she said, when her mother wanted to know the

meaning of the sigh. "It seems as if we didn't do *half* the things we wanted to do, nor see *half* the things we wanted to see."

"Never mind," her mother answered. "We shall have to come up again while Virginia and Bob are here."

"Oh, Mother, really?"

"Yes," she answered, "I have promised the boys that we will all come up to London to see the Christmas pantomimes. They have never seen them, although you and Edith have, many times."

"But, Mother," Edith said eagerly, "do take us all, anyway! I know that Virginia and Bob would love it. *Nothing* is more fun than the Christmas pantomimes!"

The two guests were received and welcomed most cordially by the other members of the family, which included the two little boys, the father, and a dear old grandfather. It was a very happy family group that gathered at the dinner table that night. And because they were a very modern English family, the young people did most of the talking. A great many plans were made for the vacation days which lay before them.

It would take too long to tell how they spent those days. But, finally, the day before Christmas arrived. And on that afternoon there came the solemn occasion of uprooting the fir tree from their own garden, and planting it in the big green tub which was always used for that purpose. After Christmas it would be replanted in the same spot, and would keep on growing. The American children had never heard of this custom, and they both thought it such a good one that they intended to pass the idea on when they returned to America.

Very carefully the evergreen tree was taken from its soil, roots and all, and planted in rich black earth in the green tub. "You see," Anne explained, "we just borrow our Christmas tree! This is the same tree we used last Christmas, and we feel as though it is an old friend."

"Perhaps it has been waiting patiently all year for Christmas to come again." Edith laughed.

"Just as the little fir tree did in Hans Andersen's story," offered Virginia. "Except that *this* tree won't wither and die after Christmas, as the fir tree did. It surely is a splendid idea, and this tree appreciates it, I know. What a beautiful tree it is!"

And indeed, it was a beautiful tree. After it had been placed in a corner of the big living room, the children made a trip to the attic to bring down the boxes of Christmas decorations. They were ready and eager to begin trimming the tree at once. Its large green boughs stretched out most appealingly, and they longed to place upon them the delicate tree things which they knew were carefully wrapped in tissue paper in the boxes. However, Mrs. Seymour suggested that they wait until after dinner, when the little boys had gone to bed.

When Mr. Seymour came home from town with his arms filled and pockets bulging with last-minute packages of all sizes and shapes, and his wife had quickly smuggled them all into the large closet under the stairway, and the odor of the tree in the living room had spread through all the lower part of the house, and the children caught glimpses of things very good to eat every time they peeped into the kitchen or pantry, and all of them had finally gone to the dining room to eat dinner and had found tall red candles on the table and a bunch of mistletoe tied to the chandelier, it seemed that Christmas Eve had truly descended upon them! While they were eating, a lovely sound came from outdoors.

"Oh, there are the Christmas waits!" the children exclaimed. Then everyone sat still and listened. The group of young men and women going the rounds of the town had stopped just outside the Seymours' house to sing their lovely carols. The house was brightly lighted from top to bottom, and this had been the signal for the waits to stop. How clearly their voices rang out on the cold night air!

God rest ye merry, gentlemen, may nothing you dismay . . .

The children all loved that carol, and it was all they could do to keep from chiming in with the carolers. As it was, they hummed it quietly and applauded warmly when the singers had finished it. The servant had opened the windows, and at the close of the first carol the entire family had gathered before the windows, clamoring for more music.

The waits sang several more of the beautiful carols, and ended their short concert with another one that they all loved.

Winds thru the olive trees
Softly did blow,
Round little Bethlehem
Long, long ago.

Sheep on the hillside lay
   Whiter than snow
Shepherds were watching them,
   Long, long ago.

Then from the happy sky,
   Angels bent low
Singing their songs of joy,
   Long, long ago.

For in a manger bed,
   Cradled we know,
Christ came to Bethlehem,
   Long, long ago.

As the group moved away to go on to the next place, the family clapped their hands and called "Thank you" after them.

Very reluctantly the two little boys said good night to everyone immediately after dinner, and started upstairs.

"As soon as we are ready for bed, Edie," they called to their older sister from the stairway, "we will be ready to hang up our stockings, and you come up *right* away!"

Edith promised that she would. The two girls had never ceased the custom of hanging up their stockings on Christmas Eve, and since Mother and Father were always very busy on that night, Edith managed the ceremony. And so when word came that the boys were ready for bed, she suggested to Virginia and Bob that they each get a stocking and come with them to their father's library upstairs.

In the library there was a big fireplace with a most convenient mantel, and on the mantel there were telltale holes where the nails of many Christmases ago had been driven in to hold the stockings. This year instead of four stockings there were six. When the last one had been hung, the children stood off and gazed at them with satisfaction.

"My!" Anne said, "it's nice to have so many of us at Christmas time. It's nice to have you and Bob here!"

"And it's wonderful to be here," Virginia answered warmly.

"Will you put us to bed, Bob?" the boys asked of that young man, each one taking a hand and pulling him toward the door.

"That is indeed a great honor they are conferring upon you, Master Robert," said Edith laughingly. "It has to be a *very* special person to put those boys to bed on Christmas Eve, and one they think the world of. You'll probably be sorry, though, that you were chosen. You will have to tell no less than ten times just exactly how Santa Claus comes in a sleigh across the house tops, and comes down the chimney!"

"I'll tell them ' 'Twas the night before Christmas, and all through the house not a creature——' "

"Oh, we *know* that!" the boys cried. "Tell us something else."

And so Bob went off to their room with the small boys to do the best he could to satisfy them.

All evening the Seymour parents were busy doing the mysterious things that must always be done by fathers and mothers on Christmas Eve. They stayed in the dining room, keeping the door closed. And so the children had the living room all to themselves, and the privilege of trimming the tree and the room as they chose. Grandfather had gone to bed shortly after the boys, saying as he left the room, with a merry wave of his hand, " 'Merry Christmas to all and to all a good night!' "

They took great pains in the trimming of the tree. Edith took upon herself the important task of adjusting the electric bulbs that were to light the tree. Then Bob stood on a low stepladder and placed the bright-colored glass balls, the paper cornucopias, and tinsel on the green branches, while Anne and Virginia carefully unwrapped the decorations they took from the boxes, and handed them up to him. It was with great satisfaction that they finally surveyed their work when it was done. Mother and Father were brought in from the dining room to inspect the work.

"It is beautiful, beautiful!" the always-enthusiastic mother exclaimed. And the father agreed, adding, "But I *do* think that ten thirty is late enough for young people to be up on Christmas Eve! Let's send them to bed, Mother."

They were all quite ready to go to bed and to sleep.

A wild rush and scramble to the library at an early hour of the morning, a quick identification of certain short, weird-shaped stockings, and two little boys were happy. As they sat upon the library rug and brought forth candies, oranges, nuts, and small packages of all sorts from the resourceful stockings, Mother and Father stood in the doorway. They must have been listening for just such a scramble as this, and now they stood watching the children's enjoyment. In a moment another pair of tousled heads appeared in the doorway, with a cry of "Merry Christmas!" and a kiss all round. Mrs. Seymour suggested that they waken their little guests so that they, too, might open their stockings. And soon all six of them were seated upon the floor, each with a stocking. There was much fun and laughter, and after every single thing had been examined, the parents suggested that they all return to bed for another nap before daylight.

There was a Christmas service at the church at ten o'clock, and when breakfast was over the entire family, including Grandfather, walked into town to attend the service.

Christmas dinner, contrary to the usual order of meals in England, is at noontime. Almost as soon as they had returned from church, dinner was announced. The Lewis children discovered that an English Christmas dinner was very little different from the American Christmas dinner. There was a wonderful goose and it made them think of the Cratchits' Christmas dinner in *The Christmas Carol,* as did also the beautiful plum pudding when it was brought into the dining room all ablaze and with the proverbial piece of holly to decorate it.

"Oh, that was a wonderful pudding!" someone sighed, wishing that one did not reach one's capacity quite so soon when there was still a goodly supply of pudding left on the table.

There were several special friends Edith and Anne wished to visit that afternoon, and they took their American friends along. The afternoon passed quickly, twilight descended upon them, and the children eagerly waited for tea to be over. Then would come the most exciting part of the whole day!

Tea was disposed of in some way, although eagerness and anticipation had taken away their appetites. At last everyone was ready—all gathered outside the living room door—children, parents, grandfather, guests, and servants. Father unlocked the door, which had been kept closed all day. There was a rush into the room, and there stood the Christmas tree, ablaze with its colored lights, and beautiful with its gay trimming. Of course, almost everyone had seen it except the boys, but everyone was thrilled anyway. And directly beside the tree stood a wide table piled high with packages! There were little ones and big ones, square and round and oblong ones, white and red and green ones! And under the tree there were two sleds, exactly alike. It was only a second or two until eager, boyish hands laid claim to these, and sure enough, their names were on them, with "Love from Mother and Father."

There were gifts for every individual in the household, including Virginia and Bob. Those two children were so pleased and grateful for the kind thought the others had shown them that they were scarcely able to utter intelligible words of thanks. Tears shone for a moment in Virginia's eyes as she unwrapped a very beautiful set of Dickens in leather-bound volumes from her parents. Her twin was equally pleased with the handsome camera of a special make he had been secretly wishing for. Everybody was happy. They waited patiently for each package to be opened before another one was handed out by Father, who read the names gaily, and quite as if he had never seen the packages before! The servants received gifts too. Everyone thanked everyone else, and there was such chattering and talking and laughing as had not been heard in the house since last Christmas! It was a jolly time for everybody.

When the last gift had been opened and the children had begun to calm down, Father started the usual custom of playing games. They began with some foolish, childish game, and everyone, Grandfather and servants and all, took part. For an hour or so there was a great deal of hilarity in which the Christmas tree was endangered more than once. They played "Farmer in the Dell," and when they sang "Heigh-ho the deerre-oh, the rat takes the cheese" it turned out that Grandfather was the cheese!

It was hard to bring such fun as this to an end. But Mrs. Seymour persuaded her small sons to go up to bed with a promise of a story—a story about "The First Christmas." And so Mother, Father and the boys disappeared, and only Grandfather and the children remained.

"Come, Grandfather," Anne coaxed, seating herself upon the arm of his big chair. "Tell us a story."

"About the first Christmas?" he asked, playfully patting her cheek.

"No. Tell us how *you* celebrated Christmas when you were small."

The others gathered around him in anticipation of a story. Grandfather made room on the other arm of his chair for Virginia and began:

"Now, let me see; what did we do in those days that you do not do now? Not much, I think. So that my story shall not really be a story after all, and I am very sleepy, my dears. When you get to be as old as I, you shall see that you shall need a great deal of sleep.

"However, I *will* say that when I was a lad we made quite a bit more of Christmas than you do in these days."

"But how, Grandfather? We make a lot of Christmas in our own way."

"Yes, yes. But in the olden days there was so much more entertaining done than now. When I was just a lad and living with my parents in the great house that you two girls have often heard about (it was in the north of England, and such a country house as that is not known in these parts today), we thought nothing of having as many as thirty guests at Christmastime. They came a week before Christmas, and some of them stayed a week after Christmas. My father's servants were overjoyed, preparing for and serving these guests. For weeks ahead there were preparations that would have made you think the King himself was expected! There was cooking, boiling, baking and basting! It was not the fault of the servants if the guests did not gain a bit of weight on the fare they received in my father's house. As the guests began to arrive, we children—always trying not to get in the way, of course (for that was the way children were trained in those days)—we children went about with our eyes and ears open for all the excitement that prevailed. We were not allowed to sit at table with the guests; children never did. But after our suppers had been eaten, and just before we were hustled off to bed, we would creep along the long hall and peek into the banquet room through the half-open doors. To see all of those well-dressed men and women at table, my father at the head and my mother at the foot, and all manner of foods and wines being served to them by men in handsome livery—it was the envy of our young lives!"

"But what happened on Christmas Day, Grandfather?"

"Well, let me see! Christmas was not so much of a child's day in those days, now that I come to think of it. The large Yule log was always brought in and placed in the huge fireplace in the hall, and was kept burning from sunset on Christmas Eve until after Christmas Day. (We always saved a portion of it to start the Yule fire next Christmas.) On Christmas Eve we always heard the waits sing and play their carols. They were invited into the house. There were usually three musicians with them, and sometimes there were just the musicians alone, with their harp, fiddle and flute. After they had finished playing, they went on to the next place. We were allowed to stay up a little later on Christmas Eve, and we hung our stockings by the chimney just as you do.

On Christmas we were usually given gifts of money by all our relatives. We visited a lot on Christmas Day, and at every place the visitors were given a bit of ale and Christmas cake.

"Well, children, when I think of the Christmases of those days, I believe, in spite of the lavish entertaining that was done and the immense preparations that were made, the Christmas Day *you* spend now is far more pleasant."

"Oh, I think so, too," said Anne, and the others agreed.

"It is late, and I am tired," said the old gentleman, beginning to rise, "and I wouldn't be surprised if you girls, and this young man here, were every bit as tired as an old man!"

It had been an exciting day and the young people decided that they were ready for bed.

The rest of the Christmas vacation passed rapidly. On Boxing Day they contributed to the gifts of money put in the servants' boxes, as well as those for the postman, the milkman, and even the railwaymen and cabmen. One day that stood out from all the others following Christmas was the day Mrs. Seymour took them once more to London, to see the Christmas pantomimes. The six children and Mrs. Seymour managed to see just about everything, and what a maze of merriment and fun it was! There was talking, singing, dancing, marching, joking, tumbling, gay music and laughter. They were entertained in turn by Alice in Wonderland, Ali Baba and the Forty Thieves, and, of course, dear old Punch and Judy, and many funny clowns and fat policemen. It would be impossible to describe the joy these characters brought to the two little Seymour boys. It was a day that none of them could ever forget.

Mr. Lewis had cabled from America that the children were to go back to school when their vacation had ended. Grandmother was better and he and Mrs. Lewis hoped to return to England in a few weeks.

When at last it came time for all of the children to return to school, and the last of the packing was being done and last words of advice were being given, Virginia and Bob felt reluctant to leave the lovely home. They told the Seymour family that they had never spent a happier Christmas than this one in the home of their English friends.

"I am sorry Grandmother was ill," Virginia said, "and I missed Dad and Mother, but I am *so* glad we came here!"

ELIZABETH HOUGH SECHRIST

NORWAY

Unique Christmas Customs in Norway

THE CELEBRATION OF YULE WAS PRACTICED IN THE NORTH-
ern countries long before they accepted the Christian religion.

This heathen celebration was a feast in honor of the sun,
when, in January, it seemed to renew its strength and over-
come the power of darkness (by rising high enough on the
firmament to spread its golden rays over the country).

During the two weeks of this festival only the most necessary work was to be done. Implements with wheels, like
wagons and the spinning-wheels, must rest. To let a wheel

move was a sacrilege against the holy sun, as it might indicate that they wanted the sun-wheel to move faster.

Fish, bird, and beast must have perfect peace during the two-weeks' celebration of Yule. Therefore, every trap and snare must be taken away, and even the fish-nets must be removed from the ocean and rivers.

The great Christmas peace—resting over the whole creation—must be observed, or woe be unto the transgressor. Selma Lagerlöf tells a beautiful story about a bear that was kind enough to give Christmas lodging in its winter den to a farmer who was lost in the storm.

But when the farmer returned the next day with his gun in order to kill the bear, the bear killed the man, and even his wife thought this was a righteous punishment, because her husband had attempted to kill the bear before the Christmas festival was over.

From these twelve holy Christmas days the people took forebodings for the coming year. Every day they wrote on one of the big logs under the rafters a sign indicating the kind of weather for that day. If it was stormy the first day, the whole first month of the next year would be stormy, etc.

From this they have the proverb, "If the Christmas signs do not fail."

At the end of the twelve holy days came the climax of the great festival. The days were getting longer and a huge wheel would be rolled from farm to farm.

When the Christian religion was introduced, Christmas was celebrated a couple of weeks earlier than Yule, and thenceforth heathen and Christian customs were mixed.

All Christmas preparations must be finished before St. Thomas' Day, December 21st. By that time sufficient wood had to be cut to last over the two-weeks' celebration. If this were neglected, St. Thomas would come and take away the ax. Likewise, must all baking, brewing, and butchering be ready by that day, otherwise they will have some mishap with everything. A cake was put on a shelf for St. Thomas before five o'clock Christmas Eve.

How we as children used to count the weeks, days, and finally the hours before Christmas! But when everything was in order in the house, barn, stable, and store-house, and we could put up the Christmas sheaves for the birds, then we knew the great feast was drawing nigh.

It was now a question for everyone to get a bath, put on clean underwear and the best clothes, including any new garment made for Christmas. Whereupon the whole family would gather in peace and contentment and partake of the Christmas Eve dinner which usually consisted of short ribs, different kinds of bread and cake, and rice pudding. Into the rice pudding had been put one almond. The one who found this almond on his plate would be the first one to get married. Everyone had to leave some pudding on his plate for the dead, who were certain to call during the night and get their share of the Christmas food. This was left on the table in great quantity and variety; but the dead do not eat like us mortals. They only want "the spirit of the food," hence when morning came everything looked as though it were untouched. It was, however, not only the good spirits that would visit the house Christmas night. The ghostly pranks of the evil spirits consisted in going from farm to farm and taking revenge on their enemies. This wild host brought fear and trembling wherever they went, for the transgressor was put through the most cruel punishment.

Even the Christmas ram or goats must be fed. In some places they would put some barley in a shoe and place it under the bed. Most of the time they could see that he had

been eating a little during the night. But if the ram did not touch it, he was offended at something and would bring bad luck during the year. At a certain farm a cow died during the spring and the lady of the house was positive that it was her husband's fault because he had neglected to feed the Christmas ram.

In the parish Elverum, they knew just where the Christmas ram lived. He moved from place to place during the winter until Christmas Eve, when he finally managed to get under the dining room table. The last thing before they went to bed they would sweep very carefully under the table, and the first thing in the morning on Christmas Day, they would see if the ram had left any grain there. If they found some it would be a good year, providing the grain was good.

If this was poor, it would be a poor crop that year; but if they did not find any, it would be crop failure.

But it is not only the supernatural beings that must be provided with extra food at Christmas. In some places they would give the domestic animals an extra meal about five o'clock Christmas Eve. In feeding them they would say, "Eat well, keep well; this is Christmas Eve."

Then they would feed the cattle salt out of a cowbell. This would help them next summer to come home from the pasture in the evening of their own accord.

Different prognostications were taken from grain and salt that had been placed on the hot hearth Christmas Eve.

What has been stated in this article so far are mostly antiquated customs no longer to be found; but there is one nice custom in use, not only all over Norway, but among the Norwegians who have emigrated to foreign countries. At Christmas I have seen in Minnesota, Wisconsin, Illinois, and North Dakota sheaves of grain put upon poles out in the yard, or on top of the barn. Then I knew that Norwegians were living there.

These sheaves are the largest and best that could be selected at threshing time. They should be put up on a spruce pole on which a large tuft of branches must be left at the top. This makes a nice place where the birds can rest after their meals. The snow should also be removed from a large circle on the lawn, and on this bare spot the birds will dance between meals, and thus get up their appetites for the next repast.

When everything was finished Christmas Eve, the dishes

washed and the house set in order for Christmas Day, and all the old brooms had been carefully hidden in order to prevent the witches from riding them; when for a similar purpose the fire-shovel and tongs had been put away; then the head of the household would go out to see if there were many sparrows in the Christmas sheaf. If there were many, it would be a good corn year; but if a sparrow sat down in the sheaf before all the work connected with putting it up had been finished, it was an omen that someone in the family would soon die.

On Christmas Eve, when darkness had conquered the light, then the fear of evil beings crept upon one. In order to drive away the witches and other uncanny beings, they went out in the yard and fired a shot. This has been transformed into "shooting in Christmas," or a Christmas salute. The young men go from farm to farm and sneak up close to the window while shooting, in order to make the people quake.

But they could not be offended, as such a visit was considered an honor, and the husbandman would go and invite them in for refreshments.

As it was commonly believed that the witches would be riding around in the air on their brooms that evening, the people were afraid that they might come down the chimney. In order to prevent this they would burn dry spruce, which would send out so many sparks that it would keep away the uninvited guests, or if one put salt in the fire it would serve the same purpose.

It was not considered safe to go to bed that evening without leaving a light burning, because all evil beings were usually active on this holy night. Sometimes they made an extra large candle that would last all night, and this they left burning on the hearth with a circle of salt around it. Both the candle and the salt were consecrated.

But in most places they would burn the "Yule Log," as all evil shuns the bright light. This custom of burning the "Yule Log" was in olden times transferred from Norway into England.

Many other safety devices were resorted to on Christmas Eve. Steel had to be put over the stable and barn doors; and with a brush dipped in tar, the sign of the cross was made over the different doors.

These customs, mostly used in the rural districts, are now passing away; but of those that are still in use one might be mentioned.

They leave a light burning in the window all Christmas night as a sign that any traveler is welcome for food and shelter.

The table is set all the time during the two weeks of Christmas festivities, and visitors as well as members of the family can help themselves at any time to food and drinks.

DR. J. O. HALL

SWEDEN

Yuletide Joys

IT WAS THE DAY BEFORE CHRISTMAS—SUCH A BUSY DAY IN the Ekman household. In fact, it had been a busy week in every household in Sweden, for before the tree is lighted on Christmas Eve every room must be cleaned and scrubbed and polished, so that not a speck of dirt or dust may be found anywhere.

Gerda, with a dainty cap on her hair, and a big apron covering her red dress from top to toe, was dusting the pleasant living room; and Karen, perched on a high stool at the dining room table, was polishing the silver. The maids were flying from room to room with brooms and brushes; and in the kitchen Fru Ekman and the cook were preparing the lut-fisk and making the rice pudding.

The lut-fisk is a kind of smoked fish—salmon, ling, or cod—prepared in a delicious way which only a Swedish housewife understands. It is always the very finest fish to be had in the market, and before it reaches the market it is the very finest fish that swims in the sea. Every fisherman who sails from the west coast of Sweden—and there are hundreds of them—gives to his priest the two largest fish which he catches during the season. It is these fish which are salted and smoked for lut-fisk, and sold in the markets for Christmas and Easter.

When Gerda ran out into the kitchen to get some water for her plants, she stopped to taste the white gravy which her mother was making for the lut-fisk.

Then as she danced back through the dining room to tell Karen about the pudding she sang:—

> Away, away to the fishers' pier,
> Many fishes we'll find there,—
> > Big salmon,
> > Good salmon:
> Seize them by the neck,
> Stuff them in a sack,
> And keep them till Christmas and Easter.

"Hurry and finish the silver," she added, "and then we will help Mother set the *smörgåsbord* for our dinner. We

never had half such delicious things for it before. There is
the pickled herring your father sent us, and the smoked
reindeer from Erick's father in Lapland; and Grandmother
Ekman sent us strawberry jam, and raspberry preserves, and
cheese, and oh, so many goodies!" Gerda clapped her hands
so hard that some of the water she was carrying to her plants
was spilled on the floor. "Oh, dear me!" she sighed, "there
is something more for me to do. We'd never be ready for
Yule if it weren't for the Tomtar."

The Tomtar are little old men with long gray beards and
tall pointed red caps, who live under the boards and in the
darkest corners of the chests. They come creeping out to do
their work in the middle of the night, when the house is still,
and they are especially helpful at Christmastime.

The two little girls had been talking about the Tomtar
for weeks. Whenever Karen found a mysterious package
lying forgotten on the table, Gerda would hurry it away
out of sight, saying, "Sh! Little Yule Tomten must have left
it."

And one day when Gerda found a dainty bit of embroidery under a cushion, it was Karen's turn to say, "Let
me have it quick! Yule Tomten left it for me." Then both
little girls shrieked with laughter.

Birger said little about the Tomtar and pretended that
he did not believe in them at all; but when Gerda set out
a dish of sweets for the little old men, he moved it down
to a low stool where they would have no trouble in find-
ing it.

But now the Tomtar were all snugly hidden away for the

day, so Gerda had to wipe up the water for herself, and then run back to her dusting; but before it was finished, Birger and his father came up the stairs—one tugging a fragrant spruce tree, the other carrying a big bundle of oats on his shoulder.

"Here's a Christmas dinner for your friends the birds," Birger told Karen, showing her the oats.

For a moment Karen's chin quivered and her eyes filled with tears, as she thought of the pole on the barn at home where she had always fastened her own bundle of grain; but she smiled through her tears and said cheerfully, "The birds of Stockholm will have plenty to eat for one day at least, if all the bundles of grain in the markets are sold."

"That they will," replied Birger. "No one in Sweden forgets the birds on Christmas Day. You should see the big bundles of grain that they hang up in Rattvik."

"Come, Birger," called his father from the living room, "we must set up the tree so that it can be trimmed; and then we will see about the dinner for the birds."

Gerda and Karen helped decorate the tree, and such fun as it was! They brought out great boxes of ornaments, and

twined long ropes of gold and gleaming threads of silver tinsel in and out among the stiff green branches. They hung glittering baubles upon every sprig, and at the tip of each and every branch of evergreen they set a tiny wax candle, so that when the tree was lighted it would look as if it grew in fairyland.

But not a single Christmas gift appeared in the room until after all three children had had their luncheon and gone to their rooms to dress for the afternoon festivities. Even then, none of the packages were hung upon the tree. Lieutenant Ekman and his wife sorted them out and placed them in neat piles on the table in the center of the room, stopping now and then to laugh softly at the verses which they had written for the gifts.

"Will the daylight never end!" sighed Gerda, looking out at the red and yellow sky which told that sunset was near. Then she tied a new blue ribbon on her hair and ran to help Karen.

"The postman has just left two big packages," she whispered to her friend. "I looked over the stairs and saw him give them to the maid."

"Perhaps one is for me," replied Karen. "Mother wrote that she was sending me a box."

"Come, girls," called Birger at last; "Father says it is dark enough now to light the tree." And so it was, although it was only three o'clock, for it begins to grow dark early in Stockholm, and the winter days are very short.

All the family gathered in the hall, the doors were thrown

open, and a blaze of light and color met their eyes from the sparkling, shining tree. With a shout of joy the children skipped round and round it in a merry Christmas dance.

The cook in her white apron, and the maids in their white caps, stood in the doorway adding their chorus of "ohs" and "ahs" to the general excitement; and then, after a little while, the whole family gathered around the table while Herr Ekman gave out the presents.

It took a long time, as there were so many gifts for each one, and with almost every gift there was a funny rhyme to be read aloud and laughed over. But no one was in a hurry. They wondered and guessed; they peeped into every package; they admired everything.

When the last of the gifts had been distributed, there was the dinner with the delicious lut-fisk, the roast goose, and the rice pudding. But before it could be eaten, each one must first taste the dainties on the *smörgåsbord,* a side-table set out with a collection of relishes.

There was a tiny lump in Karen's throat when she ate a bit of her mother's cheese; but she swallowed them both bravely, and was as gay as anyone at the dinner table.

All the boys and girls in Sweden are sent to bed early on Christmas Eve. They must be ready to get up the next morning, long before daylight, and go to church with their parents to hear the Christmas service and sing the Christmas carols. So nine o'clock found Karen and the twins gathering up their gifts and saying good night.

"Thanks, thanks for everything!" cried the two little

girls, throwing their arms around Fru Ekman's neck; and Karen added rather shyly, "Thanks for such a happy Christmas, dearest Tant."

"But this is only Christmas Eve," Gerda told her, as they scampered off to bed. "For two whole weeks there will be nothing but fun and merriment. No school! No tasks! Nothing to do but make everyone joyous and happy everywhere. Yuletide is the best time of all the year!"

ETTA BLAISDELL MCDONALD AND
JULIA DALRYMPLE

HOLLAND

The Festival of Saint Nicholas

WE ALL KNOW HOW, BEFORE THE CHRISTMAS TREE BEGAN
to flourish in the home life of our country, a certain "right
jolly old elf," with "eight tiny reindeer," used to drive his
sleigh-load of toys up to our house tops, and then bound
down the chimney to fill the stockings so hopefully hung
by the fireplace. His friends called him Santa Claus, and
those who were most intimate ventured to say "Old Knick."
It is said that he originally came from Holland. Doubtless
he did; but, if so, he certainly, like many other foreigners,
changed his ways very much after landing upon our shores.
In Holland, Saint Nicholas is a veritable saint, and often

appears in full costume, with his embroidered robes, glittering with gems and gold, his mitre, his crozier and his jeweled gloves. *Here* Santa Claus comes rollicking along on the 25th of December, our holy Christmas morn. But in Holland, Saint Nicholas visits earth on the 5th, a time especially appropriated to him. Early on the morning of the 6th he distributes his candies, toys and treasures, then vanishes for a year.

Christmas day is devoted by the Hollanders to church rites and pleasant family visiting. It is on Saint Nicholas' eve that their young people become half wild with joy and expectation. To some of them it is a sorry time, for the saint is very candid, and if any of them have been bad during the past year, he is quite sure to tell them so. Sometimes he carries a birch rod under his arm and advises the parents to give them scoldings in place of confections, and floggings instead of toys.

It was well that the boys hastened to their abodes on that bright winter evening, for in less than an hour afterwards the saint made his appearance in half the homes of Holland. He visited the king's palace, and in the self-same moment appeared in Annie Bouman's comfortable home. Probably one of our silver half dollars would have purchased all that his saintship left at the peasant Bouman's; but a half dollar's worth will sometimes do for the poor what hundreds of dollars may fail to do for the rich; it makes them happy and grateful, and fills them with new peace and love.

Hilda Van Gleck's little brothers and sisters were in a high state of excitement that night. They had been admitted into the grand parlor; they were dressed in their best, and had been given two cakes apiece at supper. Hilda was as joyous as any. Why not? Saint Nicholas would never cross a girl of fourteen from his list just because she was tall and looked almost like a woman. On the contrary, he would probably exert himself to do honor to such an august-looking damsel. Who could tell? So she sported and laughed and danced as gaily as the youngest, and was the soul of all their merry games. Father, mother, and grandmother, looked on approvingly; so did grandfather, before he spread his large red handkerchief over his face, leaving only the top of his skull cap visible. This kerchief was his ensign of sleep.

Earlier in the evening all had joined in the fun. In the general hilarity there had seemed to be a difference only in bulk between grandfather and the baby. Indeed a shade of solemn expectation now and then flitting across the faces of the younger members had made them seem rather more thoughtful than their elders.

Now the spirit of fun reigned supreme. The very flames danced and capered in the polished grate. A pair of prim candles that had been staring at the Astral lamp began to wink at other candles far away in the mirrors. There was a long bell rope suspended from the ceiling in the corner, made of glass beads netted over a cord nearly as thick as your wrist. It generally hung in the shadow and made no sign; but tonight it twinkled from end to end. Its handle of crimson glass sent reckless dashes of red at the papered wall, turning its dainty blue stripes into purple. Passersby

halted to catch the merry laughter floating, through cur-
tain and sash, into the street, then skipped on their way with
a startled consciousness that the village was wide awake.
At last matters grew so uproarious that the grandsire's red
kerchief came down from his face with a jerk. What decent
old gentleman could sleep in such a racket! Mynheer Van
Gleck regarded his children with astonishment. The baby
even showed symptoms of hysterics. It was high time to attend to business. Madame suggested that if they wished to
see the good Saint Nicholas, they should sing the same loving invitation that had brought him the year before.

The baby stared and thrust his fist into his mouth as
Mynheer put him down upon the floor. Soon he sat erect,
and looked with a sweet scowl at the company. With his
lace and embroideries, and his crown of blue ribbon and
whale-bone (for he was not quite past the tumbling age)
he looked like the king of the babies.

The other children, each holding a pretty willow basket,
formed at once in a ring, and moved slowly around the
little fellow, lifting their eyes, meanwhile, for the saint to
whom they were about to address themselves was yet in
mysterious quarters.

Madame commenced playing softly upon the piano; soon
the voices rose—gentle, youthful voices—rendered all the
sweeter for their tremor:

> Welcome, friend! Saint Nicholas, welcome!
>   Bring no rod for us, tonight!
> While our voices bid thee, welcome,
>   Every heart with joy is light!

Tell us every fault and failing
We will bear thy keenest railing,
So we sing—so we sing—
Thou shalt tell us everything!

Welcome, friend, Saint Nicholas, welcome!
Welcome to this merry band!
Happy children, greet thee, welcome!
Thou art glad'ning all the land!

Fill each empty hand and basket,
'Tis thy little ones who ask it,
So we sing—so we sing—
Thou wilt bring us everything!

During the chorus, sundry glances, half in eagerness, half in dread, had been cast towards the polished folding doors. Now a loud knocking was heard. The circle was broken in an instant. Some of the little ones, with a strange mixture of fear and delight, pressed against the mother's knee. Grandfather bent forward, with his chin resting upon his hand; grandmother lifted her spectacles; Mynheer Van Gleck, seated by the fireplace, slowly drew his meerschaum from his mouth, while Hilda and the other children settled themselves beside him in an expectant group.

The knocking was heard again.

"Come in," said Madame, softly.

The door slowly opened, and Saint Nicholas, in full array, stood before them. You could have heard a pin drop! Soon he spoke. What a mysterious majesty in his voice! what kindliness in his tones!

"Karel Van Gleck, I am pleased to greet thee, and thy honored vrouw Kathrine, and thy son and his good vrouw Annie!

"Children, I greet ye all! Hendrick, Hilda, Broom, Katy, Huygens, and Lucretia! And thy cousins, Wolfert, Diedrich, Mayken, Voost, and Katrina! Good children ye have been, in the main, since I last accosted ye. Diedrich was rude at the Haarlem fair last fall, but he has tried to atone for it since. Mayken has failed of late in her lessons, and too many sweets and trifles have gone to her lips, and too few stivers to her charity box. Diedrich, I trust, will be a polite, manly boy for the future, and Mayken will endeavor to shine as a student. Let her remember, too, that economy and thrift are needed in the foundation of a worthy and generous life. Little Katy has been cruel to the cat more than once. Saint Nicholas can hear the cat cry when its tail is pulled. I will forgive her if she will remember from this hour that the smallest dumb creatures have feelings and must not be abused."

As Katy burst into a frightened cry, the saint graciously remained silent until she was soothed.

"Master Broom," he resumed, "I warn thee that boys who are in the habit of putting snuff upon the foot stove of the school mistress may one day be discovered and receive a flogging——"

(Master Broom colored and stared in great astonishment.)

"But thou art such an excellent scholar, I shall make thee no further reproof.

"Thou, Hendrick, didst distinguish thyself in the archery match last spring, and hit the Doel, though the bird was swung before it to unsteady thine eye. I give thee credit for excelling in manly sport and exercise, though I must not unduly countenance thy boat racing since it leaves thee too little time for thy proper studies.

"Lucretia and Hilda shall have a blessed sleep tonight. The consciousness of kindness to the poor, devotion in their souls, and cheerful, hearty obedience to household rule will render them happy.

"With one and all I avow myself well content. Goodness, industry, benevolence, and thrift have prevailed in your midst. Therefore, my blessing upon you—and may the New Year find all treading the paths of obedience, wisdom, and love. Tomorrow you shall find more substantial proofs that I have been in your midst. Farewell!"

With these words came a great shower of sugar-plums upon a linen sheet spread out in front of the doors. A gentle scramble followed. The children fairly tumbled over each other in their eagerness to fill their baskets. Madame cautiously held the baby down in their midst till the chubby little fists were filled. Then the bravest of the youngsters sprang up and burst open the closed doors—in vain they peered into the mysterious apartment—Saint Nicholas was nowhere to be seen.

Soon there was a general rush to another room, where stood a table covered with the finest and whitest of linen damask. Each child, in a flutter of excitement, laid a shoe upon it. The door was then carefully locked, and its key hidden in the mother's bedroom. Next followed good night kisses, a grand family procession to the upper floor, merry farewells at bedroom doors—and silence, at last, reigned in the Van Gleck mansion.

Early the next morning the door was solemnly unlocked and opened in the presence of the assembled household, when lo! a sight appeared proving Saint Nicholas to be a saint of his word!

Every shoe was filled to overflowing, and beside each stood many a colored pile. The table was heavy with its load

of presents—candies, toys, trinkets, books, and other articles. Every one had gifts, from grandfather down to the baby.

Little Katy clapped her hands with glee, and vowed, inwardly, that the cat should never know another moment's grief.

Hendrick capered about the room, flourishing a superb bow and arrows over his head. Hilda laughed with delight as she opened a crimson box and drew forth its glittering contents. The rest chuckled and said "Oh!" and "Ah!" over their treasures, very much as we did here in America on last Christmas Day.

With her glittering necklace in her hands, and a pile of books in her arms, Hilda stole towards her parents and held up her beaming face for a kiss. There was such an earnest, tender look in her bright eyes that her mother breathed a blessing as she leaned over her.

"I am delighted with this book, thank you, father," she said, touching the top one with her chin. "I shall read it all day long."

"Aye, sweetheart," said Mynheer, "you cannot do better. There is no one like Father Cats. If my daughter learns his 'Moral Emblems' by heart, the mother and I may keep silent. The work you have there is the 'Emblems'—his best work. You will find it enriched with rare engravings from Van de Venne."

(Considering that the back of the book was turned away, Mynheer certainly showed a surprising familiarity with an unopened volume, presented by Saint Nicholas. It was strange, too, that the saint should have found certain things made by the elder children and had actually placed them upon the table, labeled with parents' and grandparents' names. But all were too much absorbed in happiness to notice slight inconsistencies. Hilda saw, on her father's face, the rapt expression he always wore when he spoke of Jacob Cats, so she put her armful of books upon the table and resigned herself to listen.)

"Old Father Cats, my child, was a great poet, not a writer of plays like the Englishman, Shakespeare, who lived in his time. I have read them in the German and very good they are—very, very good—but not like Father Cats. Cats sees no daggers in the air; he has no white women falling in love with dusky Moors; no young fools sighing to be a lady's glove; no crazy princes mistaking respectable old gentlemen for rats. No, no. He writes only sense. It is great wisdom in little bundles, a bundle for every day of your life. You can guide a state with Cats' poems, and you can put a little baby to sleep with his pretty songs. He was one of the greatest men of Holland. When I take you to the Hague I will show you the *Kloosterkerk* where he lies buried. *There* was a man for you to study, my sons! he was good through and through. What did he say?

> Oh, Lord, let me obtain this from Thee
> To live with patience, and to die with pleasure!

"Did patience mean folding his hands? No, he was a lawyer, statesman, ambassador, farmer, philosopher, historian, and poet. He was keeper of the Great Seal of Holland! He was a—Bah! there is too much noise here, I cannot talk"—and Mynheer, looking with astonishment into the bowl of his meerschaum—for it had "gone out," nodded to his vrouw and left the apartment in great haste.

The fact is, his discourse had been accompanied throughout with a subdued chorus of barking dogs, squeaking cats, and bleating lambs, to say nothing of a noisy ivory cricket that the baby was whirling with infinite delight. At the last, little Huygens taking advantage of the increasing loudness of Mynheer's tones, had ventured a blast on his new trumpet, and Wolfert had hastily attempted an accompaniment on the drum. This had brought matters to a crisis, and well for the little creatures that it had. The saint had left no ticket for them to attend a lecture on Jacob Cats. It was not an appointed part of the ceremonies. Therefore when the youngsters saw that the mother looked neither frightened nor offended, they gathered new courage. The grand chorus rose triumphant, and frolic and joy reigned supreme.

Good Saint Nicholas! For the sake of the young Hollanders, I, for one, am willing to acknowledge him, and defend his reality against all unbelievers.

MARY MAPES DODGE

BELGIUM

Christmas in Belgium

PIETER WAS EXCITED. HE HAD SOME VERY PLEASANT NEWS
to tell to his friend Jeanne today, and he was so eager to
tell it he could scarcely wait another moment. He held his
hand up to his eyes and looked far down the street to see
if she were coming.

Pieter was a happy-looking little boy with shining blue
eyes. Today he was dressed in a bright jacket, wide baggy
trousers, black stockings, and wooden shoes or *kloefen,* as
they are called in Belgium. He wore a small black hat on
his curly head. He stood outside his home, a tall red-tiled
house on a funny little crooked street in Antwerp. Pieter

100

loved his father's house, and all the other houses on the street. He thought Antwerp quite the nicest city in the whole world with its sturdy old houses and beautiful churches, museums and art galleries. Best of all he loved the Antwerp Cathedral which was not far from his home.

Pieter knew that the Cathedral was the largest in all of Belgium. His father had told him that it was five hundred years old. He liked to stand off from the Cathedral and look up at its tall and delicately carved spire, four hundred and two feet high! But the part that Pieter loved best of all was the chime of ninety-nine bells. What marvelous bells they were! He had been told that the largest of them required the strength of four men to ring it. Pieter, as he listened to the chimes ringing out over the city to call people to church, often wished that he might help to ring them.

On the walls of the Cathedral are some of the world's most famous pictures. When Pieter strolled into the quiet church on a weekday, as he often did, there were two of these pictures that he always gazed at for a long time. And, small as he was, the beauty and sadness of the two paintings made him happy and sad at the same time. They were "The Elevation of the Cross" and "Descent from the Cross" painted by Reubens. After he had looked at the pictures he would walk softly along the cool wide aisles of the great church and ponder over many things. He would stand entranced before the figures of the Christ Child, of the Holy Mother, and of John the Baptist. Of the three figures, the last was the one before which he had gone that very morning and stood a long, long time. And we shall soon see why he was so interested in John the Baptist.

At last Pieter's waiting was rewarded when his friend Jeanne came into sight. Jeanne was the little girl who delivered milk in Pieter's neighborhood. Her father was a dairyman, and Jeanne, with her cart and dogs, delivered the milk to his customers. Her milk-cart clattered gaily over the rough stones of the street. Today the dogs which pulled the bright little cart were coming with what seemed to be more than their usual speed. They were running! And the milk-cart was lurching from side to side, with Jeanne running and trying to keep up with it. Ah, now Pieter could see the cause of the dogs' excitement. A cat was running before them, and the dogs had forgotten about their mistress, about the milk cans, which were bouncing up and down in the cart, and everything else. They were good dogs; but after all, what dog will not run in hot pursuit when a cat crosses its path? When the cat dashed up to where Pieter was standing, he made a dive and caught it.

"Why!"—and Pieter held the cat at arm's length for a moment, then burst into laughter. Then he turned around,

opened the front door of his home, and thrust the animal inside, saying, "That is *my* pussy your dogs are chasing, Jeanne."

But at that moment there was a real catastrophe. The dogs had wheeled about so suddenly that the cart turned over, upsetting milk cans and straw all over the street. Pieter made haste to set the cart upright, and he and Jeanne arranged the cans of milk carefully on their beds of straw. Jeanne scolded her dogs severely and they hung their heads in shame.

And now Pieter could keep his good news no longer.

"Jeanne, what do you think? At last the church officials have decided upon the boy who is to take the part of John the Baptist in the Christmas Procession. And it is *I*, Jeanne! Just think of it. Last year I was too small. But this year I have grown so tall that they have chosen me!"

Pieter's eyes sparkled with joy and excitement as he and Jeanne talked about the coming Christmas Procession. Jeanne was very glad for her little friend. As they talked of it, it seemed to them both that they could not possibly wait for Christmas Eve to come—three whole weeks off!

But there were only a few days to wait for the day when St. Nicholas would come. For in Belgium he comes on December sixth, which is the feast day of the good saint, and rides through the cities and towns on a white pony. It is then, and not on Christmas, that he distributes toys and candy to the children who have been good. On that day Pieter was walking the boulevards with his mother when he saw Jeanne. She was dressed in her best clothes and clasped a doll in her arms. The boulevards and streets were overflowing with people. Pieter left his mother for a moment to stop and speak to Jeanne and show her the fine drum St. Nicholas had left for him.

"He must have thought I was a good boy," Pieter explained to Jeanne, "because he took the vegetables which I left for his pony, and filled the basket under the chimney with all kinds of candy and toys. And one of my gifts was hidden in a cabbage, Jeanne! What do you think of that? It was not a real cabbage, but I certainly thought it was until I looked very closely. It was just an imitation, but it looks so very real it would fool anyone. And inside, when I opened it, I found a penknife from St. Nicholas."

It seemed to Pieter as if the days between December sixth and Christmas Day would never pass. But they did, of course, and Christmas Eve found Pieter all ready and waiting impatiently to join the Procession. As he waited for his mother to finish dressing, he was wondering if Jeanne would be proud of him when she saw him marching in the Procession.

As for Jeanne, she stood anxiously waiting for the Procession to pass, and little chills of anticipation ran down her spine. She had stood a long time because she wanted to be very sure of having an advantageous position on the sidewalk. She wanted to see everything. The bells all over the city were ringing, and loudest of them all were the grand old bells of the Cathedral calling the people to Mass. The streets were crowded with people. With such a crowd as this to watch the Procession, one wonders if there will be any people left to march!

But, ah, yes! Look at them! Here they come at last. There are hundreds of children in the Procession, from the tiniest ones who can sing just a wee bit with their soft voices, to the larger girls who are really young ladies. The young girls are in groups. Some of them are clad in white, some in lilac, others in blue or pink. Each group bears an emblem, and each girl grasps a bright ribbon streamer. These streamers are attached to the central figure of the group—a shrine, a crucifix, or an image of some saint.

The streets are strewn with flowers and bright-colored fragments of paper, making a carpet for the Procession. Groups of children, singing to the music of the bands, and chanting priests, all pass on their way to the great Cathedral. After the priests come the chariots, dazzling the eyes of the beholders with their splendid cloths of gold and silver. Each chariot carries some image or crucifix.

And now Jeanne is excited indeed, for here comes little Pieter! The men are baring their heads and all stand in silence as John the Baptist passes! In one hand he carries a cross, and with the other he leads a white lamb by a blue ribbon. Pieter, his face shining bright and smiling, sees Jeanne among the spectators, and his eyes sparkle with joy. "What a happy face has our little John the Baptist!" exclaim some of the people nearby. "Yes, a sweet face; happy, and yet serious, too."

Jeanne almost dances, because she is so happy over

Pieter's success that she can hardly stand still. She is thinking that she will tell him, after it is all over, that he is the finest John the Baptist who has ever marched in the Procession!

And now the Procession nears the end. Last of all comes the Cardinal! He is gorgeous in gold embroidery, rare old lace and jewels. He walks sedately under a gold and purple baldaquin which is held over him by four men, and is surrounded by acolytes in their white robes and scarlet hats.

They have all marched on; the Procession is over. The people pass in throngs to the church.

After the Mass is over, the people will return to their homes. Christmas candles will be lighted for the Christ Child. Families will gather together and sing Christmas hymns. And then, after it is all over, our little "John the Baptist" will be tired enough to go to bed.

His day is over; his part has been played; he has marched in the Grand Procession! And as he closes his eyes they are filled with visions of the bright lights of the church, and his ears still ring with the sound of the thousands of voices which sang in the Cathedral that night:

"Adeste fideles, laeti triumphantes!"

ELIZABETH HOUGH SECHRIST

FRANCE

Christmas in Paris

AMONG THE FRENCH, CHRISTMAS IS NOT THE FAMILY FEAST that it is with us. The great fête-day here, when all the members of a family meet, and presents and greetings are exchanged, is New Year's Day.

On this day many of the tradesmen leave their offerings, a pot of cream from the *laitier,* chocolates or fruit from the grocer. A week later, on the occasion of the fête des Rois —Twelfth Night—the baker sends you a special flat cake, made of a very flaky pastry, and peculiar to this season, called a *galette,* usually with a tiny doll, a little china *sabot,* or a bean baked in it for luck. The one who finds the doll, the *sabot,* or the bean is the "king" or "queen" of the evening. Each tradesman then expects a Christmas-box. Everyone wishes you a *"Bonne Année,"* and no one must be forgotten, from the concierge, whose tip is generally in proportion to the rent of the tenant, down to the girl who brings home the laundry-work.

New Year's Day is the grown-up feast, but Christmas is kept especially for the children, who look for the *"Petit Noel,"* the Christ Child, to come down the chimney, instead of Santa Claus, and fill their shoes with presents.

For weeks beforehand the big shops have altered their departments to make room for the hosts of toys and Christmas decorations. Each shop has some attraction—perhaps a giant Christmas tree, twenty or thirty feet high, hung with presents, to be distributed later to small sufferers in the hospitals; or a group of life-size automatic figures—a chef in white cap and apron, who dips a fork into a huge copper cauldron, and fishes up everything imaginable, from a stuffed monkey to a cauliflower, with a human face and eyes that wink at you, to the great delight of the children who crowd there to watch.

During the few days before Christmas it is difficult to force a passage through the shops, and the toys are fascinating. The mechanical toys and the beautiful kitchen outfits that would make any little girl happy—real stoves to burn coal or alcohol, and miniature sets of copper or enamel saucepans, both tiny dolls'-house affairs and larger sizes that will readily cook—are among the most attractive. Paris is the home of dolls, for the French doll is famous the world over, and everything that a doll might require in furniture, clothes, or toilet articles is to be bought for them. There are even dolls' toothbrushes, tiny flasks of dentifrice, and manicure-sets.

A feature of Paris at Christmastime are the *baraques*— small stalls or booths erected along the boulevards—at which all kinds of knickknacks are sold—sweets, mechanical toys, and all the latest novelties. It is quite like a fair, and the booths remain till after New Year's Day. All during those weeks the streets are very gay and full of people. There are street-vendors as well, and the barrows that sell holly and mistletoe. France is the country of mistletoe, and one sees it here in perfection. Everyone buys it, for a branch hung above the doorway at this season is said to bring luck to a house during the entire year. Holly is less plentiful, but the flower-sellers will take the scarlet berries and wire them into other greenery so deftly that they seem to have grown there, and the effect is quite pretty. I do not remember having seen this "made" holly anywhere else, but a good deal is sold here. It drops less quickly than the real holly, and looks rather quaint and formal.

There are no Christmas pantomimes in Paris, where as a general rule children or young people are not taken to the theatres; but a sort of fairy-play for children is often put on at this season, and there are several splendid circuses open all through the winter.

On Christmas Eve are held what are called *réveillons*— a sort of friendly gathering—when people sit up all night to welcome in Christmas. All the cafés will advertise their *réveillon,* and invite their regular customers, and many people prefer to spend the evening in this way rather than at their own homes. It is a sociable idea, and as the spirit of the season makes everyone feel friendly, it is certainly pleasanter for a stranger in Paris or anyone living alone to pass the time in such gathering, with its atmosphere of good-fellowship, than by themselves.

Midnight Mass is celebrated on Christmas Eve in most of the churches in Paris, and the service is very beautiful and impressive. Afterwards one stays to visit the *crêche,* the representation of the stable at Bethlehem, with the three shepherds, and the Star of the East hung above it, which is set there, in a corner of the church, to remind one of the first Christmas Eve and the real spirit of Christmas.

MARGERY WILLIAMS BIANCO

GERMANY

Christmas in Germany

THE APPROACH OF CHRISTMAS IN GERMANY IS HERALDED
by the Advent Wreath. In almost every home this large
Christmas wreath is made of laurel or some other evergreen
branch. In the circle formed by the wreath four candles are
placed. Then the family hang their wreath from the ceiling
by bright red ribbons. On the fourth Sunday before Christmas they light the first of the candles. On the following Sunday, a second candle is lit and by the time the Sunday preceding Christmas comes around, all four candles must be
burning.

About the same time that the Advent Wreath makes its
appearance in the house, another preparation for Christmas

is begun. When the air is filled with sweet and spicy smells from the baking of the yuletide cakes and cookies, everyone knows that Christmas is really on its way. A vast amount of these are needed for the holidays, and so the baking starts weeks ahead of Christmas. This is something that all the family shares in, for mixing the batters is a very serious affair involving a great deal of work. When a German mother bakes for Christmas she calls on all the members of the household to take a turn at stirring and beating the doughs. When the children's arms grow weary, only a reminder is needed of the delicacies that will come out of the oven to spur their muscles on to new energy.

Almost every community has its own special kind of Christmas cake. In the city of Hamburg, honey and gingerbread cookies are the favorites. In Saxony, the most popular

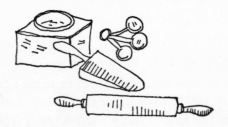

ones are baked in long narrow shapes to represent the manger of the Christ Child. These are called *Stöllen* and they are filled with currants and sprinkled generously with sugar. Another kind is made of wheat flour, sugar and butter, and bursting with fruit and nuts. *Pfefferkuchen* and *Lebkuchen* are cookies that are always baked weeks ahead to make them just right for Christmas eating. *Lebkuchen,* made with spices and nuts, are cut in the shape of hearts. Then there is a white Christmas dough cut into all sorts of fancy shapes: angels, stars, animals and people. And always there are the hard cookies called *Springerle,* which are stamped with Christmas symbols, trees and flowers. These last two kinds are used as ornaments when it comes time to trim the Christmas tree.

The legend of the first Christmas tree, which originated in Germany, tells how Winfred, an English missionary traveling in the forests of northern Germany, came suddenly upon a scene that caused him to be filled with great distress. This was at the time, many many years ago, when the people worshipped many gods and made human sacrifices to them. The people he saw in the woods were grouped under a great oak tree and were just about to slay the little Prince Asulf as a sacrifice to the god Thor. Winfred immediately, in great indignation, commanded that the "Blood oak" be cut down. This was done and, as the tree fell, a small fir tree instantly grew in its place. At the sight of this miracle, the people were filled with fear and awe. Winfred explained to them that this was the tree of Life and represented the Christ Child. Forever after, the little fir tree was shown and revered on the anniversary of Christ's birth.

There is also a German legend telling how the Christmas tree was first trimmed. The great Martin Luther, who founded the Lutheran Church, was walking home from church one night just before Christmas. His thoughts were centered on the anniversary of the Christ Child's birth. As he walked through the woods, he noticed how the bright stars in the sky, as he looked up, seemed to be twinkling on the branches of the trees. It gave him the idea of trimming the Christmas tree to make it sparkle, as though the shining stars were upon it. When he reached home he cut down a small fire tree and took it into the house. Then he attached candles to its branches and lit them. When his children gathered about the tree they agreed that the twinkling lights did, indeed, look like stars gleaming. From that time on, people put lights on their Christmas trees.

The Christmas tree is considered a very important part of the celebration in a German household. Usually the mother of the family trims it in secret so that the first glimpse of it on Christmas Eve is a surprise that the children have been eagerly waiting for. In addition to lights and balls and tinsel, cookies in fancy shapes and special kinds of candy are used to trim the tree. One of the decorations is a hard rock candy called *Kringeln* made in the shape of figure eights. Another is *Lübecker Marzipan,* a sweet almond paste candy shaped like miniature fruits and vegetables. All these sweetmeats are so tasty that it is not surprising when, after the tree has been up for several days after Christmas, much of the decoration has disappeared from the branches.

One ornament that always finds a prominent place on the tree is the tinsel angel often called the "Christ Child of Nürnberg" because it is made in that city. This bright angel wears the traditional German peasant dress but has her dress and crown generously trimmed with brass tinsel.

In some families where money is no problem, each child

has a separate small Christmas tree. But this custom is dying out in favor of the larger family tree.

German families decorate their homes with evergreens just as one would expect, but they also like to have fresh flowers about the house for the Christmas season. They like candles for decoration too. In Bavarian villages a candle glows in the front window of every house. They say the candlelight will help the Christ Child to find His way when He comes with presents for those who have served Him.

The German Santa Claus is Saint Nicholas, always shown in his bishop's robes and carrying a cross. His special day is celebrated December the sixth, so he visits houses on the night of the fifth. Instead of riding in a sleigh, he arrives in town on a white pony. The children leave hay for his pony in their shoes and next day find their shoes filled with candy and other goodies. Some boys and girls leave notes for him beside their shoes, telling him what they want for Christmas. They know that Saint Nicholas, who is so kind and good, will deliver the note to the Christ Child. For, to most German children, it is the Christ Child who is the giver of gifts. Saint Nicholas is his messenger, a reminder to the children to be good so that the Christ Child will be pleased and bring gifts to them on Christmas Eve.

In northern sections of Germany, the character of *Knecht Ruprecht* takes the place of Saint Nicholas. He wears a long beard and is dressed all in fur. The boys and girls in some places in Germany know him as *Pelznickel* and are told by their parents that if they misbehave *Pelznickel* will bring them only lumps of black coal for Christmas.

Germany is a land of wood carvers and toymakers. All who are skilled in this art turn out their best work for the products that are to be sold for Christmas. When the Christmas Fairs open, the wares that are on display are unrivaled in any country in the world. Every German becomes the proud possessor of some precious bit of work from the hands of the skilled craftsmen.

Saint Nicholas Day is usually the time for the opening of the Christmas Fairs. These are held in every large city and also in many smaller towns in Germany. The fair in the city of Nürnberg, the home of the toymakers, is the oldest in Germany. The thousands of dolls and mechanical toys on display there in the *Christkindl Markt* are wonderful to see. When the fair opens officially with the ringing of bells and the singing of carols, it is a signal for the great crowds of children accompanied by grown-ups to visit the fascinating booths full of toys and ornaments and good things to eat.

Christmas Eve comes all too soon for the mother of the family, for this is the time when all preparations come to an end and the celebration begins. When darkness falls and the first stars appear, the time has come for Mother to steal into the parlor and light the tree. Then the door is opened and all the members of the family troop in to exclaim over the beauty of the tree and to see what the Christ Child has brought. In many homes, this is the time for the visit from a *Christkind* (pronounced Kristkint), who comes into the room dressed like an angel with white robes, a golden crown and large golden wings. In his arms he carries all kinds of intriguing paper packages. These are called *Julkapp*. Each is marked with the name of some member of the family. As the gifts are distributed, children cry *"Julkapp!"* and hasten to open their packages.

Each member of the household has a separate table to hold his gifts and on each there is a plate of wonderful Christmas goodies: bon-bons, Marzipan sweets that look like real fruits and vegetables, and other candies, nuts and apples together with a sample of every kind of cooky baked in the weeks ahead of Christmas.

After the gifts are all opened, the favorite carols are sung around the tree. Then it's time for a Christmas Eve supper, usually featuring carp as the main dish.

When midnight approaches, the churches are filled with people who have not forgotten that this is the night commemorating the birth of the Infant Jesus.

Christmas Day is a family day. After a big Christmas dinner there may be visits from relatives or friends who have come to see the tree and the presents. The little ones play with their new toys and go to bed that night dreaming happily of the good *Christkind* who was so generous this year. And another Christmas has come and gone.

ELIZABETH HOUGH SECHRIST

SWITZERLAND

Christmas Customs in Switzerland

IT IS THE DAY BEFORE CHRISTMAS, AND THE DEAR LITTLE
mountain village is almost buried in sparkling, pure-driven
snow—a marvelous vision in white, with its fleckless beauty
still accentuated by the sapphire blue of the sky, the healthy
sepia-tan of the chalets, and the somber green of the stately
pines.

That indescribably sweet perfume of the Christmas season
floats through the air, and every bush and tree wears proudly
the dazzling decorations which nature has so lavishly provided in her own artistic designs. We behold a new world,

gloriously beautiful and humble in spirit at the same time; a world full of mystic charm, as it appears now in the delicate illumination of a crescent moon and its endless company of stars.

Here and there a merry tinkling of bells! Sleigh-riders homeward bound, eager to reach a friendly hearth in time for the celebration of the gladdest and greatest festival of the year—Christmas, when the *Christkindli*—the Christ-child—walks on earth.

And lo, as we look pensively down the narrow village street, there approaches a sleigh, drawn by six magnificent reindeer. Its occupant, a radiant angel—the *Christkindli*—is the poetic successor of jolly old Santa Claus, who in many parts of Switzerland, and not so long ago, used to be hailed as the generous donor of all Yuletide gifts. On *Christkindli's* sleigh, there are Christmas trees of every size, decorated with the many glittering things which are so fascinating to young hearts, and heavily laden with rosy apples, oranges, nuts, and fragrant cookies. A truly appetizing and sensible array! There are packages, too, of tantalizing shape; and with the aid of her helpers, *Christkindli* distributes trees and gifts.

Christmas trees everywhere—not a house is forgotten! And before the youngsters are allowed to play with their toys, the whole family gathers around the tree and sings some carols—heartfelt, joyous offerings to God for his sublime gift to humans. In many a home the story of the Nativity is read from the voluminous old family Bible, and the actual origin of the Christmas tree may even be brought up for discussion by some college-bred member, for no matter how isolated a Swiss village is, there is not one inhabitant who does not regard education as the greatest asset in modern life.

History indicates that it was only in the year 354 A.D. that the Roman Bishop Liberius designated December twenty-fifth as the birthday of Christ. On this day was observed the Roman feast of Saturn, when candles were not only used for illumination purposes, but were also exchanged as gifts in token of cheerfulness and good will. The Jews, too, were accustomed to burn candles at that time, which happened to be their Feast of Dedication, and it is thus not improbable that thousands of candles were burning throughout Palestine when Christ was born. Our present-day custom of burning candles on the Christmas tree is therefore of very ancient origin, and members of the Greek church actually call Christmas "The Feast of Lights."

There is a pretty legend which relates that the history of the Christmas tree dates back to the ninth century, when a certain Saint Winfred went to preach Christianity to the people in Scandinavia and Northern Germany. One Christmas Eve these people were gathered round a huge oak to offer a human sacrifice, according to the Druid rites; but St. Winfred hewed down the great tree, and, as it fell, there appeared in its place a tall young fir. When St. Winfred saw it, he said to the people:

"Here is a new tree, unstained by blood. See how it points to the sky! Call it the tree of the Christ-child. Take it up now, and carry it to the castle of your chief. Henceforth you shall not go into the shadows of the forest to hold your feasts with secret and wicked rites. You shall hold them within the walls of your own home, with ceremonies that speak the message of peace and good will to all. A day is coming when there shall not be a home in the north wherein, on the birthday of Christ, the whole family will not gather around the fir-tree in memory of this day and to the glory of God."

Since the passing of these days, the custom of the Christmas tree has found its way into the remotest corners of the

earth. Its significance and purpose have been crystallized in Christian minds and hearts, and yet there remains here and there the observance of certain quaint customs at Christmastide.

It is Christmas Eve, and after the last candle has flickered out on the tree, some of the simple peasant folk in the sequestered Swiss mountain vales begin their observance of some of the odd customs which have been handed down to them by many generations of ancestors. Grandmother hastens to the cellar for the most perfect specimen of an

onion. This she cuts into half, peels off twelve layers, one
for each month of the year to come, and in due rotation she
fills each one with salt. On the following morning the family
is able to prepare an advance weather-chart of the year,
for the peelings which contain damp salt indicate the rainy
months, and the peelings with dry salt stand, of course, for
the fair months.

And if any member of the family is courageous enough to
consult the oracle as to the length of time which is yet
allotted to him on earth, he will presently take the Bible,
and the first Psalm which strikes his eye contains in stanzas
the number of years which he is yet given to live.

If mother wishes to safeguard her chickens from all beasts
of prey, she will now proceed to the chicken-coop and clip
the wings of the fowls before midnight, but she must be
careful not to go within hearing distance of the stable where
the cattle are housed, for the hour from eleven to midnight
on Christmas Eve is the sacred time when the dumb beasts
are able to converse together—and disaster is predicted for
the inquisitive who takes it upon himself to listen.

The head of the house, too, has his duties. All day he has
been busy shoveling snow and tying bands of straw around
the trunks of the trees in the orchard; with lantern in hand,
he now makes a last round of inspection, for the trees thus
equipped in Christmas week are supposed to yield an unusually plentiful crop in the coming year.

Christmas Eve is, moreover, that time of the year when
romance reigns on earth, and while the older members of
the family are busily occupied in their own way, an un-

married son or daughter of the house will probably slip out into the clear winter's night, and, while the church-bells are calling to Midnight Mass, she or he will drink three sips from each of nine different fountains—an easy task in this land of numerous public springs. After completing this curious rite, the supreme moment in the life of the young person concerned is at hand, for, if the spell works, the future mate will surely be standing at the church door, and a regular courtship is usually begun. With the majority of the younger contingent of the congregation attending this nocturnal mass, it is, of course, quite likely that the truly chosen one just "happens" to stand at the door. As everybody of the village is acquainted with the custom, it is readily surmised by those waiting for the service to begin that their still missing unmarried friends must be "visiting the fountains" prior to their arrival at church.

And is not the Swiss winter season an ideal time? Follow that tailing party! An endless row of sleds zigzagging their way to some point where one of those typically good Swiss inns will provide a tempting dinner and dance music as well! Either can be enjoyed outdoors, for the season of white in the mountains is one long period of sunny days, where the noon temperature, in spite of ice and snow, lures to open-air picnics, and the carefully maintained Swiss rinks are more and more hailed as nature's own unparalleled ballrooms.

While the foreign winter guests are the chief figures in Switzerland's winter frolics, many experts in the manifold varieties of winter sports are recruited from the natives, for they, of course, learn skating, skiing and tobogganing when mere babies.

The week between Christmas and New Year is visiting week among the peasants of the mountain regions. Card-parties are arranged almost daily, for the Swiss are enthusiastic players of their national card game, "Jass," and it is not an uncommon sight to see three generations emerge from the same home, all equipped with skis, all bound on the same errand—a *Kaffee-klatsch* and Jass at some neighboring house. In justice to the hard-working Swiss peasant women be it said, however, that after the holidays the card-parties are replaced by knitting- and spinning-bees.

A special kind of bread is also baked at this time of the year, known as "New Year's bread," and its extra ingredients include milk, butter, eggs and raisins. That every housewife is ambitious to excel her neighbor in the quality of her product is only natural and human!

Almost every community has now its own amateur theatrical guild, presenting plays both tragic and comic with an earnestness which never fails to impress the audience. On New Year's Day is given their gala performance, and they do not have to invent any schemes to fill the house!

New Year's Eve here, as all over the world, is given to general merrymaking and when the multitude of wondrously tuneful church-bells announce the beginning of a new year in glorious, soul-stirring chorus, resounding throughout the land, bonfires will flare up on the mountain heights and young men will start threshing on some specially constructed wooden platforms above their village—a strange invocation for a good harvest to come. Members of the local singing society, and there is one to be found in the tiniest village, will now go from house to house "caroling" and offering New Year's wishes.

On the first day of the year, many a farmer will first of all consult the sky; should it be red, it is considered an omen of storms, fires, and even war. For mere good luck, too, many a person will avoid encountering a woman on New Year's morning; to meet men or children, however, is considered very fortunate.

Why do such ancient and curious customs still linger in our enlightened age? one wonders, and then remembers that they are undoubtedly relics of beliefs dating back to times when ignorance fostered superstition. And, while some people may regard the observance of such customs as "rather foolish," others find them "interesting and picturesque," and hope that they may never die out entirely.

MARIE WIDMER

ITALY

A Roman Christmas

THE CHRISTMAS SEASON WAS THE HAPPIEST TIME OF THE whole year for Nello. The school children in the city of Rome, where he lived, had only four or five days' vacation at Christmas; but Nello had three weeks; from the beginning of the Novena until after Twelfth Night, or the Feast of the Epiphany. And those three weeks were always one round of good and beautiful times for Nello. His tutor, Signor Alessandro, worked almost as hard to make Nello happy during that vacation as he did to teach him from books all the rest of the year.

126

You see, Nello was a little crippled boy. He had been lame from birth and had always walked on crutches. It made Nello's parents sad to see the difference between their son and the other sturdy boys of Italy. But Nello was gifted with a happy heart and a cheerful smile. With such attributes he won many friends and was well loved.

However, with Nello's handicap, it was impossible for him to get about as the other boys of his age did. And when vacation times came round, and Signor was ready and willing to take Nello on a series of shopping expeditions and excursions of all sorts, it certainly made the lad very happy indeed. It was little wonder that Nello looked upon Christmas as the best time of the year.

Nello and his tutor were determined to make this year the nicest Christmas of all. So they set about it by taking the carriage into town every single day, and the good-natured coachman waited patiently in his seat outside every attractive shop in Rome.

In Rome the people usually begin to do Christmas shopping as early as the first of November, while the flowers are still blooming! The stores from that time until after the New Year hold a steady stream of people. The shops are made as attractive as possible, with flowers used everywhere for decoration.

Nello and the Signor made their way carefully through the crowds, buying gifts here and there and looking at everything. There were many foreigners among the shoppers. Nello could distinguish the tongues of English, German, French and Scandinavian visitors amongst the quick chatter of his own talkative race. That made the shopping expeditions more interesting to him. Here and there he picked up a phrase or two of English, which, when repeated by him with his imitation of the accent, made the Signor laugh aloud.

Every day they bought cakes while they were out—delicious cakes for which Rome is famous—and ate them on the way home in the carriage.

As Christmas drew nearer the shops became more and more crowded, and they were obliged to keep more to the highways. On the streets they saw many different groups of children reciting Christmas poems and receiving coins from the people who gathered round to hear. What a scramble there was when Nello would toss money to them from the carriage!

Nello had an especially good time when Signor took him to the moving-picture theatres. In fact, they both enjoyed it so much that for a while they attended a different one every afternoon. This form of entertainment did not tire Nello so much as the trips through the shops.

At last, Christmas approached. The day before Christmas was a Fast Day. From sunset of the twenty-third of December until sunset of the twenty-fourth the people fasted. This was really the beginning of the celebration of Christmas, for in Italy Christmas is a solemn religious observance. On that day Nello and his tutor ceased their merrymaking. After attending early Mass they spent the remainder of the day very quietly indoors.

But at two o'clock that afternoon the Yule log, or *Céppo*,

was lighted in the fireplace and the family gathered around it. It was in this room also that the *Presepio* was placed.

The *Presepio!* It was very dear to the heart of every member of the family. From year to year they had saved it, carefully putting it away, then bringing it out again to serve for another Christmas. And it seemed dearer to them each year —more a part of them. Nello could hardly wait until the family ceremony around the *Presepio* should begin.

Presepio is the Italian word for stable or manger. But gradually it has come to be known as the word for a miniature Bethlehem, or Place of Nativity. It represents the birthplace of Christ. There are tiny figures of the Virgin Mary

and Joseph, the shepherds, wise men and angels, and also tiny animals, all cut skillfully from wood. Nello loved each figure in their little Bethlehem.

At twilight the candles around the *Presepio* were lighted, and prayers were said. The tiny manger was empty until Nello's mother, while they all watched, put the last figure of all in its place. This was the figure of the Bambino, the baby Christ. Everyone in the room crossed himself, more prayers were said, and then Nello, leaning upon his crutch, stood beside the miniature Holy City and recited some beautiful poems of the Nativity.

After the ceremony of the *Presepio,* the twenty-four-hour fast was broken by a wonderful banquet. And such things as there were to eat! Characteristic of the Italian Christmas were the delicately prepared dishes which Nello's family never failed to feast upon at this banquet on Christmas Eve.

Evergreens are not used in Italy as a Christmas decoration. But Nello's home was filled with flowers. They were everywhere—lovely chrysanthemums, violets, and bright holly berries! And, besides, there was music. Yes, music played on odd-looking bagpipes by young men who were dressed as shepherds.

After the banquet, and while the shepherds played upon their bagpipes, came Nello's happiest moment! For it was then that the Urn of Faith was brought forth. The whole family, including Nello's older brothers and their wives and children, the parents, the Signor and the servants were there to draw gifts from the Urn of Fate. It was a very large crock which held one gift for each member of the family. It was Nello's mother who began the drawing. And it pleased Nello very much when the package she unwrapped proved to be the scarf he had bought for her. Such fun as they had drawing their gifts and examining them! To be sure, almost everyone drew a blank before actually receiving his own gift, but that only served to create more merriment.

After the excitement had somewhat subsided the small children were put to bed. Even Nello was bidden to take a rest. The church services of Christmas Eve would be very long, and Nello was not so strong as the others.

But he would not have missed the Christmas Eve services for anything. When the rest of the family climbed into the carriage at ten o'clock to be taken to the church, Nello and Signor were with them.

The streets were filled with merry crowds of people, many of whom carried torches. Bright lanterns hung in all the shops, and music and flowers were everywhere.

At church there were more music and flowers! Here, the music was very beautiful. There were crowds of people. But it was very restful to Nello who sat in his place listening to the well-trained voices of the choir boys. It made him think that to sit in a lovely church and listen to beautiful music was the nicest thing in the world.

Just before midnight there was a grand Procession of the officials of the church, in all the splendor of their colorful vestments. With them they carried the figure of the Bambino. People all over the church, as it passed, knelt before it and touched or kissed its robe. As the bells tolled midnight the Procession ended, and the Bambino was placed in the manger at the front of the church where all could see it. At the same instant the beautiful voices of the choir began singing the Magnificat.

At two o'clock the Shepherd's Hymn was chanted, and soon after, Nello and his family left the church to go home. Poor Nello was glad for the support of the Signor's strong arm, for the boy was nearly asleep.

It was the custom of Nello's family to go to the services at St. Peter's Cathedral on every Christmas Day. So Christmas afternoon found them once more approaching the church door. But this time it was to the largest church in the world they were going. For St. Peter's Cathedral of Rome has the distinction of being the largest cathedral in the whole world. Nello had passed it many times and had attended services there once every year on Christmas, but it never failed to impress him with its beauty and magnificence.

The many steps approaching the Cathedral made it quite a task for the brave little boy to mount them. But he was happy to climb those broad steps, knowing what awaited him at the top. They went slowly, his mother at his one side, his father at the other, and the good tutor carrying the lad's crutches. As they walked slowly up the great steps they passed many people; people from all walks of life. Many of them, of course, were from Rome. But there were countless visitors also, and it seemed to Nello that everyone in the world must have come to this greatest of all churches to celebrate Christmas. It was very probable that most of the nations of the world were represented there that day. The peasants of Italy were there in great numbers, many of them having come from their farms and villages to Rome and to the Cathedral on a sort of pilgrimage, to worship and to receive the blessing of the Pope.

As they made their way to the huge entrance, Nello and his family were stopped a great many times by men and boys who were selling picture postcards and cheap jewelry.

"Buy, buy!" they entreated with eager voices. Many of them were crippled. Nello stopped to buy from each one of them, and by the time they had reached the entrance doors their hands were full of cards and trinkets.

Once inside the church they made their way as quickly as possible to the great church room so that Nello could be seated. On the way in, Nello passed under the magnificent dome, four hundred feet high, which, his father told him, was the workmanship of Michelangelo. And, too, they saw the huge bronze statue of St. Peter. Nello looked at it with reverence and awe. He knew that it was ancient—that no one knew what its age was exactly. He knew a part of St. Peter's foot had been worn away by the constant kissing it had received by the millions of visitors to the Cathedral. To visit the Cathedral was to visit the statue of the saint. Even now there were streams of people waiting their turn to kneel before St. Peter and pray.

The crowds in the great church today were so large that the service lacked some of the beauty and reverence of the Christmas Eve services they had attended the night before. People were coming in by the hundreds. Signor, who was seated beside Nello, whispered to him that the Cathedral was said to be able to hold more than forty thousand people. Nello sat thinking about this and listening to the music of the beautiful organ. He thought: "Forty thousand people! That is more than there are in some whole cities."

The entrance of the Pope was a thrilling part of this Christmas service. When the Procession started which preceded his arrival, Nello became so excited that he could feel his face getting hot and his hands getting cold. To him, the Pope was the grandest and most important figure in the whole world.

It was a wonderfully impressive entrance. In the Procession there were Bishops, Cardinals and other dignitaries of the church. Then there came the Pope's Guard of Honor, and about sixty noblemen of the city of Rome. The Pope sat upon a scarlet chair, supported by several men who were dressed in robes of violet. The Pope himself was attired in rich robes hung heavily with precious jewels, and his head was crowned with a jeweled tiara.

As he passed between the rows of soldiers, he held up his hand, two fingers extended, in blessing.

At last he was seated upon a raised throne at the head of the church; the choir sang the Psalm of Entrance, and the service had begun.

From Christmas Eve until the Eve of Epiphany, or the day before "Old Christmas," the observance of the Yuletide in Italy is of a religious nature. But on the Eve of Epiphany it is different. When Nello's brothers had been small, they had always placed their shoes on the hearth. But Nello, along with many other boys and girls of Rome, hung up his stocking. It was on this night that La Befana was supposed to come. She is the only one figuring in an Italian Christmas who could be compared to Santa Claus.

La Befana was a woman, and not "a right jolly old elf," either. She was said to possess a stern nature and a rather forbidding appearance. On Twelfth Night, or the Eve of

Epiphany as it is known in Italy, she entered through the chimney and into the room where the stockings were hung. She carried a cane in one hand and a bell in the other. With the bell she anounced her arrival. Thus it was that many little children in Italy would hear a bell ringing on the Eve of Epiphany and would be told to "hurry off to sleep before Befana comes!"

In the stockings of the good little boys and girls she would put gifts that satisfied their hearts' desires. But in the stockings of the bad children she would leave only *bags of ashes!* A hurried scramble early on the morning of Epiphany proved to the children whether their conduct had been approved or disapproved by the all-wise Befana.

When Nello found a bulging stocking at his bedside, with many gifts besides that would not fit into it, perhaps he felt glad that he had pleased La Befana. But when his mother came into the room while he was opening the gifts, it was *she* who received "many thanks" from the little boy, and a big hug and kiss. Was it possible that La Befana was merely a legend? It really did not matter at all to Nello. He saw the work of loving hands in those gifts, and his suspicions were many as to whose hands they might have been.

In spite of the fact that her little son was a cripple, and had very few of the advantages and good times of other boys, his mother on that morning of Epiphany read real joy and happiness in his eyes. And she thanked God then for the finest gift her son possessed, a happy heart.

As for Nello, his Christmas season is almost over. He will soon be speaking of it as "Last Christmas," and dating

happenings with "That happened just before Epiphany."
He will be thinking already of next Christmas. And during
those long months in between he will have many happy
memories of this one—shopping expeditions with his tutor,
merry crowds of people on the street; gifts, music and
flowers; and, perhaps most vivid of all, impressive church
services where he had come face to face with the true meaning of Christmas, the Birthday of the Bambino.

ELIZABETH HOUGH SECHRIST

SPAIN

Yuletide in Spain

IN SPAIN, THE LAND OF ROMANCE AND SONG, OF FROST AND
flowers, where at Yuletide the mountains wear a mantle
of pure white snow while flowers bloom gaily in field and
garden, the season's observance approaches more nearly
than in any other country the old Roman Saturnalia.

The Celts, who taught the Spaniards the love of ballads
and song, left some traces of the sun-worshipers' traditions,
but they are few in comparison with those of other European
countries. Spain is a land apparently out of the line of

Wodin's travel and influence, where one looks in vain for the mysterious mistletoe, the pretty holly and the joyful Christmas tree.

The season is rigidly observed in churches, but otherwise it loses its spirit of devotion in that of wild revelry. Music, mirth and hilarity are the leading features of the occasion, and home and family pleasures are secondary affairs.

Of course the customs vary in different provinces, some of which still cling to primitive forms of observance while others are fast adopting those of foreign residents and becoming Continental in style. But everywhere throughout the land Christmas is the day of days—the great church festival observed by all.

The *Noche-buena* or Good Night, preceding Christmas, finds the shops gay with sweets and fancy goods suitable for holiday wear, but not with the pretty gifts such as circulate from home to home in northern countries, for here gifts are not generally exchanged.

Doctors, ministers and landlords receive their yearly gifts of turkeys, cakes and produce from their dependents, but the love of presenting dainty Christmas gifts has not reached the land of the three C's—the Cid, Cervantes and Columbus.

Do you know what you would probably do if you were a dark-cheeked Spanish lad named Miguel, or a bright-eyed, light-hearted Spanish maiden named Dolores?

If you were Miguel you would don your black jacket and brown trousers, knot your gayest kerchief around your neck, and with your guitar in hand you would hasten forth to enjoy the fun that prevails in every street of every town in Spain on Christmas Eve, or, as it is known there, the *Noche-buena*.

If you were pretty Dolores you would surely wear your skirt of red or yellow, or else of striped red and yellow; your best embroidered velvet jacket—handed down from mother to daughter, and a wonderful sample of the handiwork that once made the country famous; your numerous necklaces and other ornaments. You would carefully braid your heavy tresses and bedeck your shapely head with bright flowers. Then with your *panderetta* or tambourine in hand, you too would join the merry throng that fills the air with mirthful songs and music on *Noche-buena;* for remember,

> This is the eve of Christmas,
> No sleep from now till morn.

The air is full of the spirit of unrest; castanets click joyously, tambourines jingle their silvery strains, while guitars and other musical instruments help to swell the babel of sound preceding the hour of the Midnight Mass:

> At twelve will the child be born,

and if you have not already done some especially good deed to some fellow mortal, you will hasten to clear your conscience by such an act before the bells announce the hour of its birth. As the stars appear in the heavens, tiny oil lamps are lighted in every house, and among all devout Roman Catholics the image of the Virgin is illuminated with a taper.

The streets, which in many cities are brilliantly lighted

with electricity, are crowded with turkeys awaiting pur-
chasers. They are great fat birds that have been brought
in from the country and together with quacking ducks and
cooing pigeons help to swell the sounds that fill the clear,
balmy air. Streets and market places are crowded with live-
stock, while every other available spot is piled high with
delicious fruit—golden oranges, sober-hued dates, and in-
dispensable olives; and scattered among these are cheeses of
all shapes and kinds, sweetmeats of all sorts, the choice
candies that are brought from various provinces, and quaint
pigskins of wine. No wonder everyone who can do so
hurries forth into the streets on *Noche-buena.*

If you are not tempted to stop and gaze at these appetizing exhibits, you will pass quickly on to the brightly lighted
booths devoted to toys. Oh, what a feast for young eyes!
Here yours will surely light on some coveted treasure. It
may be an ordinary toy, a drum, a horn, or it may be a Holy
Manger, Shepherds, the Wise Men, or even a Star of the
East.

It is hard to keep one's purse closed among such a surfeit
of tempting articles, and everywhere money flows freely
from hand to hand, although the Spanish are usually very
frugal.

As the bells clang out the hour of midnight, you will
hurry to join the throng wending its way to the nearest
church, where priests in their gorgeous robes—some of them
worn only on this occasion and precious with rare embroidery and valuable jewels—perform the midnight or cockcrow Mass, and where the choir and the priests chant a

sweet Christmas hymn together. What if it is late when the service ends? Christmas Eve without dancing is not to be thought of in Spain. So you go forth to find a group of Gypsy dancers who are always on hand to participate in this great festival; or you watch the graceful Spanish maiden in her fluffy skirts of lace, with her deep pointed bodice, a bright flower in her coal-black hair beside the tall comb, and her exquisitely shaped arms adorned with heavy bracelets. "Oh, what magnificent eyes! What exquisite long lashes!" you exclaim to yourself. See her poise an instant with the grace of a sylph, one slippered foot just touching the floor, then click, click, sound the castanets, as they have sounded for upwards of two thousand years and are likely to do for two thousand more, for their inspiriting click seems necessary to move Spanish feet and give grace to the uplifted arms. At first she may favor you with the energetic *fandango,* or the butterfly-like *bolero,* but on Christmas Eve the *Jota* is the universal favorite. It is danced and sung to music which has been brought down to the present time unwritten, and which was passed from mouth to mouth through many generations. Translated, the words read:

Of Jesus the Nativity is celebrated everywhere,
Everywhere reigns contentment, everywhere reigns pleasure.

the audience joining in the refrain:

Long live merrymaking, for this is a day of rejoicing,
And may the perfume of pleasure sweeten our existence.

It will probably be late into the morning before the singing, dancing, thoughtless crowd turns homeward to rest, and although it is certainly a crowd intoxicated with pleasure, it is never in that condition from liquor.

There are three masses on Christmas Day, and all devout Catholics attend one of them at least, if not all. In some places Nativity plays are given on Christmas Eve or else on Christmas Day. They are long performances, but never tedious to the audiences, because the scenes appeal to them with the force of absolute realism. On Christmas morning the postmen, telegraph boys, and employees of vocations, present to their employers and others little leaflets containing a verse appropriate to the day, or the single sentence "A Happy Christmas," expecting to receive in return a Christmas box filled with goodies of some kind.

While Spanish children do not have the Christmas tree to gather around, they do have the pretty *Nacimiento,* made

of plaster and representing the place of Christ's nativity, with the manger, tiny men and women, trees, and animals, such as are supposed to have existed at the time and place of the Nativity.

The *Nacimiento* (meaning being born) is lighted with

candles, and little folks dance gaily around it to the music of tambourines and their own sweet voices, joyously singing one of the pretty Nativity songs. Groups of children go about the streets singing these songs of which there are many.

In this pleasing custom of the *Nacimiento* one sees a vestige of the Saturnalia, for during that festival small earthenware figures used to be for sale for the pleasure of children. Although the Spanish race is a mixed one and various peoples have been in power from time to time, at one period the country was, with the exception of Basque, entirely Romanized. It is interesting to note the lingering influence of this mighty Roman nation and find in this century that some of the main features of the great Roman feast are retained in the great Christian feast at Yuletide.

Southern races were always firm believers in Fate. The Moslems reverenced the Tree of Fate, but the Romans held sacred the *urn* containing the messages of Fate. So the Spaniards cling to the urn, from which at Christmas gatherings of friends it is the custom to draw the names of the men and women whom Fate ordains shall be devoted friends during the year—the men performing all the duties of lovers. This drawing of one's Fate for the coming year creates great merriment and often no little disappointment. But Fate is inexorable and what is to be must be, so the Spanish maiden accepts graciously the one Fate thus assigns her.

After the midday breakfast on Christmas morning the people usually seek out-of-door pleasures. Among many of the old families only blood relations are expected to eat and drink together on this holy day.

Ordinarily the Spaniard "may find perfect entertainment in a crust of bread and a bit of garlic" as the proverb claims, but at Yuletide his stomach demands many delicacies peculiar to the season. The *Puchero Olla,* the national dish for dinner, must have a few extra ingredients added on this occasion. The usual compound of chickens, capons, bacon, mutton, beef, pig's feet, lard, garlic, and everything else the larder affords, is quite insufficient to be boiled together on this occasion. However, if one has no relatives to invite him to a feast, it is an easy matter to secure a Christmas dinner on the streets, where men are ready to cook for him over their *braseros* of charcoal and venders are near at hand to offer preserved fruits, the famous almond rock, almond soup, truffled turkey, or the most desirable of the season's delicacies—sea-bream, which is eaten at Christmas in accordance with the old-time custom. Nuts of all kinds are abundant. By the side of the streets, venders of chestnuts —the finest in the world—lean against their clumsy two-wheeled carts, picturesque in costumes that are ragged and soiled from long service. Rich layer-cakes of preserves, having almond icing with fruits and liquor-filled ornaments of sugar on top, are frequently sent from friend to friend for dinner.

In Seville, and possibly in other places, the people hurry to the Cathedral early in the afternoon in order to secure good places before the high altar from which to view the *Siexes,* or dances. Yes, dances! This ceremony takes place about five o'clock just as the daylight fades and night draws near. Ten choristers and dancers, indiscriminately termed *Siexes*, appear before the altar clad in the costume of Seventeenth-Century pages, and reverently and with great earnestness sing and dance an old-time minuet, with castanet accompaniment, of course. The opening song is in honor of the Virgin, beginning:

Hail, O Virgin, most pure and beautiful.

Among the ancients dancing was a part of religious services, but it is now seldom seen in churches. This Christmas dance, given in a beautiful cathedral just at the close of day, is a very impressive ceremony and forms a fitting close to the Spanish Christmas, which is so largely made up of customs peculiar to ancient and modern races.

In every part of Spain song and dance form an important part of the festivities of Yuletide, which lasts two weeks, although the laboring class observes but two days of pleasure.

The higher circles of society observe New Year as a time of exchanging calls and visiting, feasting and merrymaking. At the banquets of the wealthy every possible delicacy in the way of food is temptingly displayed, and great elegance in dress indulged in by the ladies, who wear their finest gowns and adorn themselves in priceless jewels and rare laces. But there is so much etiquette to be observed among this class of Spaniards that one looks for the real enjoyment of the season among the common classes.

In some parts of Spain bullfights are given as late as December, but cold weather has a softening effect on the poor bulls and makes them less ferocious, so unless the season proves unusually warm that favorite entertainment has to be abandoned for a time. Meanwhile in the streets and homes one may often see a father on all fours enacting the infuriated bull for his little sons to attack; in this way he teaches them the envied art of bull-fighting. The Yuletide festivities end at Twelfth Day—Epiphany—when crowds of young folks go from gate to gate in the cities to meet the Magi, and after much merriment they come to the conclusion that the Magi will not appear until the following year.

MARY P. PRINGLE AND CLARA A. URANN

RUMANIA

Christmas Cheer

NEXT TO EASTER, CHRISTMAS AND NEW YEAR ARE THE brightest holidays of the year.

The Christmas festivities begin on the twenty-fourth of December, the last of Advent, which is also a holiday. On that day *turte* are eaten in every household. This is a special kind of cake and is made of many layers of thin dough with melted sugar or honey and pounded walnuts. Sometimes bruised hempseed is used instead of sugar. The *turte* are prepared on the previous day. In the midst of her kneading the dough, the housewife walks into the yard followed by her husband who holds an ax. They approach a tree and he

147

threatens to cut it down. "It seems to me this tree is useless; it bears no fruit," he says, but his wife speaks up to save the tree.

"Oh, no," she says, "I am sure it will be as full of fruit next summer as my fingers are full of dough." They pass on to the next tree where the dialogue is repeated, and so on until many trees are visited. The man threatens; the woman saves each tree that they want to coax into fruit-bearing.

While this is clearly a pagan ceremonial, the remnant of some old custom, the *turte,* into which the dough is made, is supposed to represent the swaddling clothes of the infant Christ. Thus are paganism and Christianity brought together.

Boys are busy announcing Christmas from house to house with the greeting:

> Good-morning to Uncle Ajun!

We dress heavily, because the winters are usually severe, and begin our rounds before dawn. We carry long bags into which we pack the gifts that are offered us as we pass from house to house and repeat the old familiar greetings. Sometimes we add verses of our own and songs. We expect and usually receive some fruit or *colac* or a small gift of money. If we strike a house where the people are slow in coming forward with a gift we repeat the song again and again:

> Wake up, wake up, Great Lords,
> For we bring you great news, etc.

But if we are kept waiting too long, we are likely to break out with the chorus:

> Good-morning to Uncle Ajun:
> Do you give us, or do you not?

repeated several times.

If our patience was tried too long, we knew and could use, some humorous verses about stingy people. But sometimes all our strategy failed and we had to give up all hope and pass on to the next house to begin all over.

These greetings are called *colinde*. We began singing *colinde* on the evening of the twenty-fourth and kept them up regularly until midnight. On the thirty-first of December we changed our songs into verses appropriate for greeting the new year.

We banded ourselves into a group and learned to recite these verses, legends, and fanciful stories, under the leadership of an older boy with experience. The *colindae* are supposed to come from the Latin *calendae, festum calendarium.* Some of the verses are adaptations to Christian subjects. Other verses are quite foreign in spirit to the Christian religion. Most of them have been carried down orally from remote ages.

We changed the verses together, according to tradition, always beginning each stanza with the same lines, over and over:

Asta sare-i sare mare,	This evening is a great evening,
Florile dalbe;	White flowers;
Sarea mare-a lui Craciun,	It is the great Christmas Eve,
Florile dalbe!	White flowers!

and always ending each stanza with the same refrain:

Casa-i legea din batrani	For such is the law (custom) of old
Florile dalbe;	White flowers;
Din batrani din oameni bu ni,	From the old, the good men,
Florile dalbe!	White flowers!

These verses we chanted to the following tune:

We knew a collection of many stories, making several hundred verses in all.

We were supposed to be messengers and to have come from distant lands. In these chants we related our experiences: whom met, what gifts we received and other fabulous happenings.

Every little while the boys broke out with the shout: *La ani si la multi ani! To the new year and to many years to come!* This gave us a chance to break our subject. Many of our *colinde* narrated fanciful stories about the moon, the sun, the stars. Even the Lord sometimes figured in our recitals. Whenever we could we brought into action the householder before whose window we were singing our carols. Usually we gave him the role of the hero of our tale.

I remember, for instance, one of the *colinde* in which we recited how the Lord bathed in a river. St. John and St. Christmas were with him. It pleased the master of the house also to take a bath, and when he stepped into the river, the Lord, astonished at such daring, asks: "Whom do you rely upon, being so bold, upon me, or upon St. John or upon St. Christmas?" Our hero is not taken aback. He answers courageously: "I am not relying upon you, O Lord, nor upon either of your saints, but on my own good deeds: I married young, I built my house by the roadside, I laid my table across the road for passers-by to feed," and in our story we went on reciting how the good master of the house had spanned precipices with bridges, had dug wells in desert fields for the benefit of strangers and so on. The Lord is well pleased. He praises the good man for his deeds in this world, and promises him fair return in the next, giving him a free pass to:

> Go to Heaven untried,
> Sit down to the banquets unasked,
> Drink the glass unpledged!

We knew many *colinde* about a great variety of subjects: emperors, heroes fighting on sea or land (the masters of the house for the time being), beautiful heroines saved from danger in the nick of time, particularly one, a beautiful girl, who, lying softly in a hammock hung between the antlers of a deer, sings in a voice at once sweet and sad:

> *Lin, mai lin,*　　　　Gently, gentlier yet,
> *Crebe stretin!*　　　Three-yearling deer!

and predicts the hunter's approach, on this occasion the master of the house, their wedding, the slaying of the hart whose skin and antlers are to adorn their happy home, and so on through many stanzas of fancies and dream-weaving.

We also knew *colinde* describing in very flowery language the pleasures of the hunt, the grandeur of fabulous friendships withstanding all tests, the delights of home life, the jealous rivalry between horse and falcon or stag. To please the lover of horses we told about wondrous steeds, gorgeously harnessed, light of foot, supernaturally strong. The fancier of sheep was told of flocks of tame ewes led by a miraculous ewe, a *nasdravan,* that is, a "seer," who foretells the approach of the cruel hunter. Here we brought in the householder as the hero who saves them and receives the blessings of the mother lambs. Then we transported our hero to an enchanted home, passed him through a great wedding scene and described minutely the gorgeous feast, the dowry, the garden with the miraculous trees and flowers that awaited him!

The *colinde* we sang at night. But we were also busy during the daytime carrying from house to house *Steaua,* the Star. This is a plain, six-cornered star made of wood, which we carried around on a high wooden pole. We covered it with colored and gilt papers and frills to make it look pretty. We kept a small candle burning in the middle of our star and the light shining through the colored paper gave it a weird appearance. We also put many little bells all around the star and the pole and their merry jingle heralded our approach.

We carried the star from about the twenty-fourth of December till the end of the month. The custom is said to be a remnant of an old Roman festival, the *Atelanae* or *Satirae*.

The songs we recited while carrying the star had come down through tradition from past ages:

> Who will receive
> The beautiful star
> With many corners
> And tiny ones . . . etc.

and the melody was also traditional:

J. S. VAN TESLAAR

SERBIA, *A Republic of Yugoslavia*

Christmas at Old Luchitsa

It was wintertime, and the snow lay thick on the ground. Not for many years had there been such cold weather in the week before Christmas—our Christmas Day really comes in January, for our calendar is thirteen days behind yours. But what did we care for frost or snow? We reveled in such frost antics, and a snowball is a snowball the world over. And this year I was going to beg my father to take me with him when he went before the dawn on Christmas Eve into the forest to cut our Yule logs. I never had been before; my mother had always opposed it, saying that I was too young to be out so early in the cold, and for

154

many other reasons which she gave at full length every time I made the suggestion. But this year I made up my mind very strongly that I would go, and I managed to coax my father into my way of thinking, which was more important!

So very, very early on Christmas Eve, when it was still quite dark, the sleepy oxen were harnessed to the big kola, and Branislav and I sat in state within it, while the big father walked beside the beasts to guide them.

I was too excited to be sleepy, for this was a great event; still, I found it much colder than I had expected, and was glad to tuck my chin into the collar of my sheepskin jacket and huddle under the shelter of Branislav's broad shoulders as we went through the village and up the hill.

How dark it was under the trees, but my father had hung a lantern on the front of the kola so that the oxen could see to pick their way, and slowly and carefully up we went, till at last we reached the clearing, where my father had marked a fine young oak tree for the purpose.

"Here is the tree that will serve us," he said to Branislav, "where is the ax, my son?"

Branislav pulled the ax from the bottom of the kola, and jumped up ready to hand it to my father, who, first crossing himself three times, threw a handful of wheat at the tree, saying, "Happy *Badnyi Dan* to you," which means, "Happy Xmas Eve to you." I had to stand well out of the way while the tree was being cut down, my father taking care that it fell toward the east, for only in such case can the coming year be a lucky one for the household. All sorts of evil fortune would be sure to come to us were the woodman to make a mistake and the tree fall to the west—but that was not likely to happen when a Stoyanovitch was tree-felling!

What a crash the young oak made in the quiet forest as it fell! My father called me to him. "Come, Milosav," he said, laughingly, "thy hand shall be the one to pick up the first chip—see! there it fell. Fetch it, and carry it carefully home," and I trotted away very importantly to pick up the wood, while they began to saw the trunk into big logs, one of which was much bigger than the rest, our finest Yule log, the *Badnyak* itself.

Little by little the sky had been growing lighter, and just as we turned the kola round and began the steep descent of the forest paths, the sun began to peep over the horizon. By the time we had reached the courtyard it was broad daylight, and as they heard the sound of our wheels the other children came running out to meet us from the house. My mother came first carrying a Pogacha, which is a flat cake of pure wheaten flour.

As Branislav piled the big logs against the side of the house, she broke the cake over the biggest *Badnyak,* as these Xmas logs are called, and wished it a "happy *Badnyi Dan.*"

"*Ohé,* Milosav," she called to me, "come here, thou little one, and do not be running away with Danilo and Aleksander till thou hast drunk the warm milk. The morning is over cold for young bodies. Then thou shalt go with the others to sing the *Colleda* songs."

I was impatient to be gone, but the warm milk was very pleasant, and when I had drunk it I ran off with Yelena to join the two boys who were waiting outside the gate with a group of other children, for it is the custom in our village on Christmas Eve for the boys and girls to go from house to house singing some very old songs. They are all about a goddess named Colleda, who lived so long ago that we really do not know very much about her, but no one likes the songs any the worse for *that*.

There is one in which we ask the goddess, "To cause the cows to give us their milk abundantly, so that we, O Colleda, may bathe our little god in white milk, O Colleda."

The little god is the one whom we call Bozhitch, the Serbian word for Christmas, but some people tell us that it is the sun god whom the Serbs used to worship before they were Christians. At that time a pig was sacrificed to the sun god every Christmas, and even today every Serb, however poor he may be, eats roast pig for his dinner on that one day in the year at least. We sang our Colleda songs till we were quite tired, and then came back to the house, where there was plenty of work waiting for us. Yelena and my mother were busy all day in the kitchen, cooking all kinds of delicious dainties, among them zhito cake, which, being made out of walnuts, wheat, and sugar, was a thing Milosav never *could* resist, so that many a time that day his fingers had to be carefully watched, and now and then soundly tapped with the big iron spoon! or else, I am afraid, there would have been very little zhito cake left for any one else.

Also, he was rather fond of the special little cakes which my mother formed so cleverly into the shape of animals— sheep and pigs, lambs and chickens, just as real as could be. So they had to be watched, too, by Yelena, armed with her iron spoon, till they came out of the oven all crisp and brown, making you *long* just to nibble a little of the lamb's tail off, or the pig's ears. It was quite necessary for my mother to put them on a high shelf, where even she herself, tall as she was, could hardly reach them. We had great fun over that cooking, and I am not saying that a few tidbits did not find their way into the hands of all us children, for my mother was what you western people call a "good sport," and dearly loved to see us happy. There was plenty for us to do outdoors, too, for we had to build up a famous fire before which the Christmas pig was to roast on Christmas morning. Then that pig had to end its earthly life, and we boys helped my father to prepare it for the next stage in its career.

Danilo went to fetch a big bundle of straw from the rick, and tied it round the middle with a rope, then he laid it near the logs till it was needed, which would be after sunset. Just as the sun was dipping behind the distant Danube, we all assembled in the warm kitchen. How cozy it felt after the keen sharpness of the air outside! My mother put a pair of woolen gloves on Branislav's hands; then he opened the door and went down the wooden steps into the courtyard. After a few minutes we heard him coming back again, and now he carried in his arms the Badnyak itself.

Danilo ran to open the door, and on the threshold Branislav called, "Good morning to you all! May you have a Happy Christmas."

My mother stepped forward, holding in her hand the

piece of wood which was the first chip from the oak tree. I had carefully carried it home, and all day long it had lain in a handful of wheat. As we all replied in chorus, "May God and the Happy and Holy Christmas keep thee," she threw the wheat and the chip at the Badnyak, and we all shouted with joy because her aim was so good. My father and Branislav then carried the Badnyak to the hearth and laid it on the fire, taking care that about a foot of it stuck out from the hearth.

Now came the part of the proceedings which I enjoyed the most. My mother went out of the house, and returned carrying the bundle of straw, and we children arranged ourselves behind her in a row, each holding to the next person's jacket or frock. She then began to walk slowly about the kitchen, and from thence into the two bedrooms, throwing handfuls of straw on the floor and imitating the cluck, cluck, of a hen, while we children merrily cried *"Peyoo, Peyoo,"* as we pranced along behind her, pretending to be little chickens.

When she had finished scattering the straw on the floor, we all stood by the hearth while my father took a handful of walnuts and flung a few into each corner of the room, east, west, north and south, for Christmas comes to every part of the earth. Then he moved over to the east side of the kitchen, where earlier in the day my mother had hung a wooden box full of wheat, with a tall candle of yellow wax placed in the middle. After he had lit the candle, my father folded his arms on his breast, and we all stood with down-bent head to hear him pray to God that we might have

health and happiness in the coming year with good yield
from the fields, plenty of calves and lambs, honey in the
beehives, and milk and rich cream from the cows.

After this came the Christmas Eve supper with all kinds
of good things, fish, beans and cabbage, onions well sea-

soned with paprika, and as much good wheat bread as we
liked. And what is the greatest fun of all is that on Christmas Eve we don't eat our supper from a table covered with
a tablecloth, sitting on wooden chairs like everyday dull-
ness—instead, sacking is laid all over the straw and the
dishes are placed on that, while we sit happily on the floor
around it!

It was not long before the mother bundled us off to bed,
for it was long past our usual bedtime, and every one gets
up about four o'clock on Christmas morning. Indeed, the
grown-up people very rarely go to bed at all; for one thing,
somebody must sit up to keep the Badnyak burning prop-
erly, because it would be a most unlucky thing for the
family if by any chance that precious log stopped blazing.

The great thing on Christmas Day is to start very early
with the roasting of the pig, and the family which first
succeeds in lighting the courtyard fire and laying the pig
before it to cook, tells all the neighbors how clever it has

been by firing a pistol. I believe Danilo hardly went to sleep at all, because he was so anxious that we should be the first, and he was bitterly disappointed when the Paskitch family, five houses down the road, managed to fire their pistol just half a minute before he was ready! But that is not the end of the battle! Another pistol has to be fired when the pig has finished cooking, and is going to be taken away from the fire, and whether it was because we took particular pains with the building of our fire, or whether we turned the pig more carefully than other people I do not know, but in the end we beat the whole of the village by at least three minutes, and Danilo was so excited that he wasted quite a lot of ammunition over his cookery!

When Yelena went to draw water from the well just before the sun rose, she wished the water a Happy Christmas, throwing a handful of wheat into the well for luck. She was careful to save a cupful of the first water she drew, and with this my mother made the special Christmas cake called *chestnitsa,* in which she placed a silver dinar. There was great excitement when the time came to cut that cake, for the person who gets the coin is supposed to be the lucky one of the family for the coming year! And this year sleepy Aleksander was the fortunate person, so we all teased him, telling him that something was going to happen to the daylight so that he could have half a day more sleep as well as the night. But little did Aleksander care for our teasing, and he went to sleep after dinner just the same as usual.

Now we were all gathered round our brightly-blazing log-fire waiting for our special Christmas visitor who must come and "let Christmas in." We all hope he won't be late, for until the *polaznik* has been, nobody else—even the priest himself—or the King if he had happened to be in Luchitsa —must enter the house.

However, our *polaznik,* who was Todor Myatovitch, a neighbor's son and a favorite companion of our Branislav, was an obliging boy, and quite soon we heard his knock at the door. As we opened it, he ran in, a handful of wheat in his fist, some of which he threw at each one of us, and some into every corner of the room, saying, "Christ is born," and, as my mother threw some wheat over him in return, we all answered, "Verily, He is born."

Todor went over to the hearth and picked up the shovel, with which he struck the Badnyak so hard that thousands of sparks flew up the chimney, saying, as he struck, "May you this year have many oxen, many horses, many pigs, many sheep, much honey, all possible good fortune and happiness on this house." Then he put his arms on my father's shoulders, and they kissed each other. After this, Todor went back to the hearth and knelt down, crossing himself reverently, and kissing the end of the Badnyak which had been left sticking out from the hearth, after which he laid a coin on the log as his Christmas gift.

As he was doing this, Yelena went quietly into the bedroom and came back with a wooden stool, which she placed before Todor, that he might sit down. But just as he was preparing to take a seat Danilo snatched the chair away and poor Todor fell to the ground!

Now, does that seem to you rather a rude way to treat

a guest? I dare say it does, but Todor didn't think us a bit rude, for he knew what to expect! You see we Serbs believe that by his fall, the *polaznik* fastens to the ground all the good wishes he has uttered in our house that day. So, naturally, Todor does not mind.

But I expect you would be puzzled if you saw my mother wrapping him up in a thick blanket, and Todor sitting quietly in it for at least two minutes, while we all stood watching him! That means that we shall be fortunate all the year in having thick cream on our milk, and when Branislav and Danilo—who are going to be our shepherds for this next year—kiss each other across the blazing logs, we know that the affection of the mother sheep for their lambs is made sure. You see we take every precaution to keep things in good order!

But now the hungry Milosav is sniffing the roast pig, and after Danilo has had the happiness of firing off his pistol before anyone else in the village, the dainty dish is brought in and set down all smoking hot upon the table. Yelena carries in a taper for everyone to hold and lights her own at the fire, then we stand quietly round holding our lights aloft till my father recites a prayer. Then we kiss each other, saying: "Peace of God be between us today. Christ is born, truly He is born, let us bow before our Christ."

What a merry Christmas dinner we have with Todor as our guest—he the best singer in all Luchitsa, ready to give us which one of our favorite songs we should ask for without any bashfulness at all, for he is just like our own brother. He will stay with us all day till evening comes, telling tales, playing his fiddle and singing. And with the snow falling thickly outside, what place so cozy as our warm kitchen, the Yule logs crackling on the hearth, and the firelight dancing on the white walls, lighting up as it reaches them the ring of happy faces in the Christmas circle?

E. C. DAVIES

ETHIOPIA

Christmas in Ethiopia

CHRISTMAS HAS BEEN CELEBRATED IN ETHIOPIA, OR ABYS-
sinia, as it used to be known, for many hundreds of years,
for Christianity was introduced into this country in 330 A.D.
The observance is so entirely different from any we know it
is probable that if we were to visit Ethiopia at Christmas
we would see little to remind us of that day in our own
country. Christmas is celebrated there on January the sev-
enth instead of December twenty-fifth.

An Ethiopian Christmas centers round the church. There
are many very old churches. Some of them are hewn from

rock. Very often the church is built square with a court surrounding it. The sanctuary is always square and stands in the center of the building. The altar, crudely constructed of wood, holds a slab or two of marble or, more often, pure gold. The Ark is covered with gold and precious gems.

Lalibela is the "Jerusalem of Ethiopia" and on Christmas the city is crowded with pilgrims from every part of the country. On Christmas Eve the hillsides surrounding the city are literally covered and swarming with people. Most of them remain outdoors all night praying and chanting, and waiting for the dawn of Christmas Day.

On Christmas morning there is a grand procession from the church to the hilltop where the liturgy is celebrated on the Coptic Church's copy of the Ark of the Covenant. The Procession consists of thousands of priests, monks and nuns, all chanting. The robes of the priests are gorgeous in color. The Ark itself is carried by four men, for it is very heavy. The crowds along the way of the Procession are tremendous. Three young men open the way with whips which they lash from left to right. After the religious ceremonies the priests dance. The throngs of people are fed with bread and mead which have been blessed by the priests. This puts everybody in high spirits. And so the day is spent in dancing, sporting and feasting. The men feast on raw meat, a custom among the Ethiopians which most people would not consider an appetizing fare for Christmas or any other day.

ELIZABETH HOUGH SECHRIST

AUSTRALIA

Christmas in Australia

THERE ARE THREE TYPES OF PEOPLE TO BE CONSIDERED IN discussing Christmas in Australia. First, there are the aborigines, the native colored people who are mostly uncivilized and unchristianized, and therefore do not celebrate Christmas at all. Second, there are the bushmen, the white country folk who till the soil and work in the Australian bush. The bushmen are mostly English. Third, there are the English people of the cities and towns.

The bush folk are very hard workers. When Christmas comes (and it comes in the hottest season of the year there), they enjoy a holiday. If some members of the family happen to be off in the hills shearing or taking care of the flocks, they come home for Christmas. Naturally the folks at home prepare a wonderful Christmas dinner. There is a great slaughtering of pigs and chickens and baking of cakes and making of puddings. The youngsters decorate the house with huge ferns and palm leaves and hang green foliage over the front door. The day is spent in visiting, chatting and eating. At night the neighbors are apt to drop in, then there is dancing to a concertina and lots of fun. The next day, which is Boxing Day as in England, is an occasion for sports. The whole family drive to the sports-meet and take their lunch along for a picnic. The boys and girls look forward to Boxing Day even more than Christmas, for it is sure to be jolly from start to finish.

The people of the cities observe Christmas in only a half-hearted way, for it is likely to be a scorching hot day, and it comes in the very midst of summer vacations, when many people are away at vacation resorts or visiting friends. However, among many families in Australia there is an earnest attempt to celebrate Christmas in the English fashion. Gifts are exchanged at the breakfast table, and then there is a Christmas service at church. A Christmas dinner of roast beef or fowl is eaten at noon. Usually the remainder of the day is spent at the beaches with an appetizing picnic supper out-of-doors, and this part of Christmas Day would remind us of our Fourth of July.

For several days before Christmas, decorations for the house can be bought in the shops or on the street in the form of greens and flowers. The houses on Christmas Day are filled with flowers. Two of these are the Christmas Bush and the Christmas Bell. The first, which grows in great profusion, is a multiple of tiny flowers growing in soft, hazy clusters. It is red and green. The Christmas Bell is a red bell fringed in yellow with bright green leaves. These flowers are quite appropriately in fullest bloom for the Christmas season.

ELIZABETH HOUGH SECHRIST

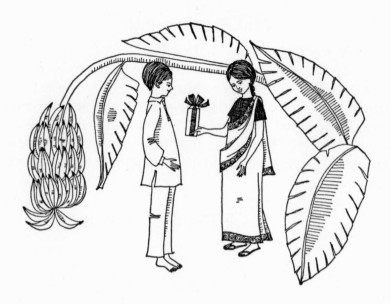

ASIA

Christmas in Asia

IN INDIA

CHRISTMAS IN INDIA IS NOT A HOLIDAY, FOR TO MOST OF the people of India the birthday of Christ has no significance. They go on with their work as though the day were like any other. But the people who do observe Christmas get up very, very early Christmas morning, around two o'clock, and sing their way to church. There they sing hymns and hold services until the crack of dawn.

In the mission compounds there is always a great party to which everybody interested is invited. The Indians call this a *tamasha*. The guests have the time of their lives, for there is always entertainment and, most important of all, refreshments are served! It is a regular Christmas party, with a tree and a small gift for everybody. The Christmas tree would probably surprise American children, for more often than not it is a banana tree with the great bunches of bananas still growing upon it! At some of these *tamashas* a pageant depicting the Nativity is enacted.

IN JAPAN

Christmas was introduced in Japan by the Christian missionaries, and for many years the only people who celebrated it were those who had turned to the Christian faith. But now the Christmas season in Japan is full of meaning and is almost universally observed. The idea of exchanging gifts seems to appeal strongly to the Japanese people. The tradesmen have commercialized Christmas just as our western shops have done. For several weeks before the day, the stores shout Christmas. There are decorations and wonderful displays of appropriate gifts for men, women, and children—especially children.

The story of the Child Jesus born in a manger is fascinating to the little girls of Japan, for they love anything that has to do with babies. In the scene of the Nativity they become familiar for the first time with a cradle, for Japanese babies never sleep in cradles.

Many of our own customs in observing Christmas have been adopted by the Japanese. Besides exchanging gifts they eat turkey on Christmas Day, and in some places there are even community Christmas trees. They decorate their houses with evergreens and mistletoe, and in some homes Christmas carols are sung gaily.

In Japan there is a god or priest known as *Hoteiosho,* who closely resembles our Santa Claus. He is always pictured as a kind old man carrying a huge pack. He is thought to have eyes in the back of his head. It is well for the children to be good when this all-seeing gentleman is abroad.

New Year's Day is the most important day of the whole calendar in Japan. On New Year's Eve the houses are cleaned thoroughly from top to bottom, and are decorated for the morrow. When everything has been made clean and neat the people of the house dress themselves in their finest clothes. Then the father of the household marches through the house, followed by all the family, and drives the evil spirits out. He throws dried beans into every corner bidding the evil spirits withdraw and good luck enter.

IN CHINA

Christmas has been celebrated in some sections of China for four hundred years, but most Chinese have never heard of it. However, where Christian customs are still observed, it is a day of happiness and excitement. The little girls receive dolls in odd-looking stockings which they hang up Christmas Eve just as their western cousins do. These stockings are made by sewing three pieces of muslin together, and are roomy enough to hold the toys that Santa Claus is good enough to bring them. Santa Claus in China is known as *Lan Khoong-Khoong* which means Nice Old Father. Still another name for him is *Dun Che Lao Ren,* Christmas Old Man. The Chinese people are very fond of the bright colors of the Christmas decorations they adopted from their friends the missionaries. They like the red holly berries and green leaves, and the bright tinsel and lights of the Christmas tree, and to these decorations they have added their colorful Chinese lanterns. On Christmas Day they ex-

change gifts, but these gifts must be in accordance with custom. Silks, jewels and other valuable gifts may be given only to members of the immediate families. Gifts of food or cut flowers are customary for friends or distant relatives.

Christmas in China is ushered in, by those who observe it, with a marvelous display of fireworks. The people enjoy themselves heartily with feasting and singing, and are entertained by Chinese jugglers and acrobats, mingling their native entertainment with the celebration as it came to them from the missionaries.

IN CEYLON

In Kandy, Ceylon, there is a most grotesque celebration on Christmas Eve. The scene is bright with the light of many lanterns and torches, and huge bonfires. The ceremony begins with the beating of drums; fireworks are displayed, and a very curious devil dance is performed. The natives' costumes, which are of every color of the rainbow, add to the glamour of the occasion.

Among the Christian mission students, Christmas carols are sung and the usual Christmas observance is held in the churches.

IN SYRIA

Among the Syrians Christmas is strictly a religious observance. The people celebrate the Birthday of Christ with great reverence. They place candles in the windows to light the Christ Child's way to His Birthplace in Bethlehem, Judea. The Syrians believe that on the Eve of Epiphany the trees bow their heads at midnight in reverence to the Christ Child.

IN BAGHDAD, IRAQ

Most of the people of Baghdad are Moslems, but there are also many Christians, who observe Christmas reverently in their homes.

In the courtyard of a Syriac home on Christmas Eve there is an unusual ceremony in which the whole family takes part. One of the children in the family reads the story of the Nativity from an Arabic Bible, while the other members of the family hold lighted candles. As soon as the story has been read, a bonfire of dried thorns is lighted in one corner of the courtyard, and the future of the house for the coming year depends upon the way the fire burns. If the thorns burn to ashes the family will have good fortune. While the fire is burning a Psalm is sung, and when it is reduced to ashes everyone jumps over the ashes three times and makes a wish.

On Christmas Day a similar bonfire of thorns is built in the church. While the fire burns, the men of the congregation chant a hymn. Then there is a procession in which the officials of the church march behind the Bishop, who carries an image of the Infant Jesus upon a scarlet cushion. The long Christmas service always ends with the blessing of the people. The Bishop reaches forth and touches a member of the congregation with his hand, putting his blessing upon him. That person touches the one next him, and so on, until all have received "the Touch of Peace."

IN IRAN

Christmas in Iran is known as the Little Feast. (Easter is known as the Great Feast.) For the first twenty-four days of December, those days preceding Christmas, a great fast is observed, during which no meat, eggs, milk or cheese are eaten. It is a time of peace and meditation; a time for attending services at the church. But when the fast is over the feast is begun. The fatted calf is killed and plenty of meat is prepared for the great Christmas dinner.

Christmas Eve is the last day of the fast. Almost before dawn on Christmas Day the people attend Mass to receive Communion, and not until they have received the bread and wine blessed by the priests are they permitted to break fast.

The children of Iran have never heard of Santa Claus, and gifts are not exchanged at Christmas, but they are sure to receive a new suit of clothes, which they proudly wear all during the happy Christmas week. A popular dish for Christmas Day is the *harasa,* a kind of chicken stew. It is cooked in such large quantities that it is very likely to last the whole week.

Iran, or Persia as it was called, played an important part

in the history of the first Christmas, for it was from there the three Wise Men came. They were Magians, who studied the stars, and when they saw the Star of Bethlehem they followed it and came to the stable where the Child Jesus lay in a manger.

IN TURKEY

Most of the people of Turkey are Moslems and, of course, do not celebrate Christmas at all. But among the Christian Turks there is a feast which lasts for three days. There is

much visiting and entertaining during that time. The Turks are famous coffee drinkers and a great quantity of coffee is consumed Christmas Week. The people are exceptionally hospitable. Everyone who comes to the house is given coffee, sweetmeats and fruit, and sometimes meat and *lebban* (sour milk) of which they are very fond.

ELIZABETH HOUGH SECHRIST

PALESTINE

Christmas in Bethlehem

DURING THE CHRISTMAS SEASON, WHEN THE THOUGHTS OF
the civilized world turn to Bethlehem, many will wonder
how the people there keep this greatest religious holiday.
Very few American children can ever visit the little city
among the Judean hills. Yet a number of travelers from
America and Europe come to the Holy Land every year, to
be among those who on Christmas Day crowd the streets of
the little city nestled among its fig trees and olive orchards.

It is a little city, and it does not take many people to
crowd it; but, besides being the birthplace of Jesus, it is the
birthplace of Israel's great warrior-king, David.

Bethlehem today has less than twenty thousand inhabi-

178

tants, and in appearance is not attractive. The streets are too narrow for vehicles; in fact, there is but one street in the town wide enough for carriages, and it is so very narrow that they cannot pass each other in it. The streets were made for foot travelers, donkeys and camels.

Bethlehem is about five miles south of Jerusalem. Leaving the larger city by the Jaffa Gate, we take a carriage and ride rapidly over the fine road built but a few years ago. The carriage we are in and those we meet are wretched affairs. The horses are to be pitied, first, because they are not well cared for, and second, because their drivers are regular Jehus who drive them "furiously" up hill and down. In less than an hour we are in the market place of Bethlehem, in front of the Church of the Nativity.

Let us suppose we have arrived on Christmas Eve, in time to wander about and to become acquainted with the little city.

Of course it has changed in appearance since the time of the birth of Christ. It is larger, and better built. Now, as then, the houses are of stone, and, as cities and customs change but little in the East, we may safely infer that modern Bethlehem houses are much like those of nineteen hundred years ago. Perhaps some of the old buildings that were in existence so long ago may still be standing. Of course the great Church of the Nativity was not then erected, nor were any of the large religious buildings we see. These are the memorials of a later date, built in honor of Him whose earthly life began here. One would have to be unmindful of his surroundings and very unimaginative not to wonder what the place was like on that night the anniversary of which we are celebrating.

We know that then, as on this December 24, it was filled with people. But those people had come for a different purpose. Augustus Caesar, the master of the then known world, had issued an imperial decree ordering a general registration of all his subjects. This was for the purpose of revising or completing the tax lists. According to Roman law, people were to register in their own cities—that is, the city in which they lived, or to which their village or town was attached. According to Jewish methods they would register by tribes, families, and the houses of their fathers. Joseph and Mary were Jews, and conformed to the Jewish custom. It was well known that he and Mary were of the tribe of Judah and family of David, and that Bethlehem was their ancestral home. Accordingly, they left the Nazareth home, in the territory of Zebulun, and came to David's "own city," in the territory of Judah.

They came down the east bank of the Jordan, crossed the river at Jericho, and came up among the Judean hills and valleys till they reached Bethlehem. It was a long journey, and a wearisome one; and, on arriving, a place of rest was the first thing they sought.

Evidently they had no friends living in the place; or, if they had, their houses were already filled. It was necessary that shelter be had, and immediately. In the khan, or inn, there was no room; so there was nothing to do but occupy a part of the space provided for cattle. It was not an unusual thing to do, and is often done today in these Eastern villages. In fact, they were about as comfortable there as in any khan. At a khan one may procure a cup of coffee and a place to lie down on the floor, but each guest provides his own bed and covering. This was all Joseph and Mary could have obtained in the inn, had there been room for them. And here in Bethlehem, in a stable, or a cave used for stabling animals, Jesus was born, and Mary "wrapped Him in swaddling-clothes, and laid Him in a manger."

There is one short walk we should take before entering the Church of the Nativity and the cave beneath it. This is to the Field of the Shepherds, about a mile east of the church, and the traditional place where the shepherds watched their flocks on that momentous night. This may not be the exact place where the angels appeared, but there is no reason why we may not accept the tradition that has placed the event here. It has often been wondered why the shepherds had their flocks out all night in the wintertime; and the wonder is easily satisfied when we know that these were not ordinary flocks of sheep nor ordinary shepherds. These flocks were those specially selected for sacrifice in the Temple at Jerusalem, at the great Passover season, and were kept in the fields all the year. The shepherds were specially appointed.

Some time during that winter night the shepherds were dazzled by a light more brilliant than the stars, and roused by voices not of earth. The Christ, whose future sacrifice their flocks were to symbolize, was born; and the angels were singing the good tidings. These shepherds were the first to hear and to spread the marvelous news.

Because of the event the angels were heralding, men have built the great Church of the Nativity in Bethlehem, and, indeed, all the great Christian churches and cathedrals of the world. It is because of this that people from every country in Europe and America will join the throng of native

Christians in the "City of the Nativity," and rejoice in memory of the angels' song. It is because of this that there is today so much of "peace on earth" and "good will toward men."

And now we return in time to see the procession of bishops, priests, and people that is forming in the square in front of the church. Each is dressed in his most gorgeous robes. Turkish soldiers line both sides of the street to keep the way open for the procession to pass. The Latin Patriarch of Jerusalem has just arrived. The procession of priests, carrying banners and immense candles, meets him, then turns, and all go into the Latin Chapel through the main entrance. Following, we are surprised to find the main entrance so small. It can admit but one at a time, and that one must stoop to enter. From the masonry it can be seen that the entrance was once much larger. The reason for the change was that the Moslems at one time did all in their power to injure and annoy the Christians, and even used to ride on horseback into the very church. The door, therefore, was made small to protect the church from this sacrilege.

Once inside, we see we are in a very ancient structure. Part of the masonry dates from the time of Constantine, who built a magnificent basilica on this site, about the year 330 of our era. All we can see of the oldest work, however, probably dates from not later than Justinian's time, about 550 A.D. In any case, the church is a venerable building, and it has witnessed some stirring scenes. In it Baldwin the Crusader was crowned King of Jerusalem. It has been repaired a number of times; and once, when it needed a new roof, King Edward IV of England gave the lead to make one. This was about the year 1482. The lead roof did good service for about two hundred years, and might have lasted much longer had not the Moslems melted it up to make bullets. However, another roof was soon provided.

Inside, the building consists of a nave and double aisles. The aisles are separated by two rows of columns made of red limestone. These columns have plain bases, and are surmounted by Corinthian capitals. They are nineteen feet high, and at the top of each a cross is engraved. The church is now owned by the Latin, Greek and Armenian Christians.

Religious services will be held all night in the Latin

Chapel of St. Catherine. At midnight a solemn mass will be said by the Patriarch of Jerusalem. The chapel is full of people, many of whom are sitting on the floor.

Before the procession descends into the Grotto of the Nativity we make our way there, so as to have a better view.

Originally it was simply a natural cave in the limestone rock. Now little of the native rock is seen. Marble slabs cover the floor and line the walls. The ceiling, which is about ten feet high, is resplendent with thirty-two brass lamps. Their light enables us to examine the many pictures, portraying scenes in the life of Jesus, which the devotion of Christians has hung about the walls; but these pictures are generally very poor specimens of art. At the east end of the cave there is a small recess in the rock, before which hang fifteen lamps. In the floor of this recess a bright silver star is inlaid; it is nearly worn away by the constant kissing it receives. Around the star is an inscription in Latin, which tells us that "Here, of the Virgin Mary, Jesus Christ was born."

Turning just a little to the right from this Place of the Star, and descending a few steps, we are in a small chamber called the Grotto of the Manger. The original manger is, of course, not here; it probably never was preserved, and many stories about it are inventions of a much later date. Here, also, is a little altar on the place where the Wise Men from the East prostrated themselves before the infant Jesus. These three—the places of the birth, the manger and the adoration—are all in what is called the Chapel of the Nativity.

Passing out of this chapel by the steps leading into the

Greek Church of St. Mary, we are again in the streets of Bethlehem.

It is a relief to get away from the glare of lamps, the smoke of candles and the heavy odors of burning incense, and to breathe again the fresh air blowing over the Judean hills. The streets are very quiet, for all not in the church have retired to their homes. Occasionally people leave the church, and are driven away in their carriages to Jerusalem, though most visitors remain all night. We can wander through the streets and over the neighboring hills, for the clear moon makes it almost as bright as day.

How peaceful it all is! Indeed, it seems a most suitable place for the coming to the world of "The Prince of Peace."

Faint streaks of the dawn are beginning to show in the sky above the hills of Moab. Rapidly they grow longer and brighter, and soon it is daybreak, and we know that it is Christmas in Bethlehem.

But we miss much of the accustomed joy of the day. At home there would be good cheer, the companionship of loved ones, and the giving and receiving of gifts. Here there is little of this. The home life of the people is different from ours. Christmas Day in Bethlehem is not the Christmas Day we know; it is full of religious ceremonies, and when these are over young and old go back to their accustomed life. The faces of the boys and girls I saw in Bethlehem last Christmas were not faces as I should have seen in any city or village in America. And I knew the reason. It was because Christmas to them was much the same as any other day of the year. And so it requires more than Bethlehem to make Christmas what we like to have it. It requires loving home life and the presence of the spirit of the Christ Child in the heart. And yet, who would not be glad to spend one Christmas eve and day where He who made the glad day possible was born?

EDWIN S. WALLACE

ABOUT THE AUTHOR

Elizabeth Hough Sechrist became interested in writing for children while she was a Children's Librarian in Bethlehem, Pennsylvania. Each year she was asked by boys and girls, teachers and librarians, for information on Christmas in other lands. Because of the lack of material, she began to collect and write on the subject herself, and the resulting book, CHRISTMAS EVERYWHERE, has been popular in schools and libraries for many years.

After nine years' experience in Bethlehem and Pittsburgh libraries, Mrs. Sechrist gave up her work to devote her time to writing, editing and lecturing on children's books—and, incidentally, to keeping house in York, Pennsylvania.

She claims the days are never long enough!